Chapter Ninetee...

ALGEBRA
1. Number Operations
a. The Commutative Rule

A **Commutative Operation** is where the order of the sum can be changed and it will still give the same answer.

Example: Demonstrate a commutative operation.

$$3 + 5 = 8 \longrightarrow 5 + 3 = 8$$

3 and **5** can be reversed but still add up to **8**. The operation is commutative.

Example: Are all operations with **2** and **4** commutative?

$2 + 4 = 6 \longrightarrow 4 + 2 = 6$ Addition and
$2 \times 4 = 8 \longrightarrow 4 \times 2 = 8$ multiplication are commutative.

$4 - 2 = 2 \longrightarrow 2 - 4 = -2$ Subtraction and
$4 \div 2 = 2 \longrightarrow 2 \div 4 = 0.5$ division are **not** commutative.

Exercise 19: 1   Commutative? Write yes or no:

1) $3 - 7$ _no_   2) 9×3 _yes_   3) $5 + 8$ _yes_

4) $6 \div 2$ _no_   5) 4×7 _yes_   6) $5 \div 8$ _no_

7) $7 - 5$ _no_   8) $8 \div 2$ _no_   9) $3 + 2$ _yes_

10) $9 - 2$ _no_

Record your Score out of ten here → $\frac{10}{10}$

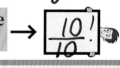

b. Directed Numbers

The term **Directed Numbers** is used of numbers when their positive or negative signs matter. (See Maths Workbook 1.)

Positive Numbers (+) are <u>greater than zero</u>. A number with no sign in front of it is known as a positive number. **Negative Numbers** (–) are <u>less than zero</u>. All negative numbers must have a negative sign in front of them.

c. Adding and Subtracting

Straightforward **Adding and Subtracting** takes place along the number line. Remember: count gaps not numbers.

Example: | What is **7** take away **10**? Answer: **-3** |

←—————— Subtracting   Adding ——————→

-8 -7 -6 -5 -4 ⊝ -2 -1 0 1 2 3 4 5 6 ⑦ 8

There are some additional rules that need to be understood. If two signs **between** directed numbers **meet each other** they are replaced by one sign. It can be summed up as: When signs are the **same** the result is always **positive** (+). When signs are **different** the result is always **negative** (–).

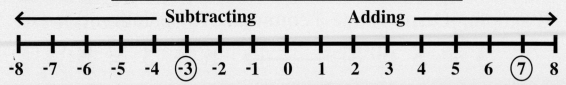

Positive (+) and **Negative** (–) ——→ **Negative** (–)
Negative (–) and **Positive** (+) ——→ **Negative** (–)
Positive (+) and **Positive** (+) ——→ **Positive** (+)
Negative (–) and **Negative** (–) ——→ **Positive** (+)

Example: | Show directed number combinations of **3 & 4**. |

+3 + +4 is 3 + 4 = 7 | +3 + -4 is 3 − 4 = -1
+3 − -4 is 3 + 4 = 7 | +3 − +4 is 3 − 4 = -1
-3 + +4 is -3 + 4 = 1 | -3 + -4 is -3 − 4 = -7
+3 − -4 is -3 + 4 = 1 | -3 − +4 is -3 − 4 = -7

Exercise 19: 2   Calculate the following:

1) **+9** + **+5** = +14   2) **-5** + **-8** = +13

ae

11+
Maths
Numerical Reasoning

WORKBOOK **6**

Dr Stephen C Curran

Edited by Dr Tandip Singh Mann & Anne-Marie Choong

This book belongs to

Siyona Bhandari.

Accelerated Education Publications Ltd.

Contents

19. Algebra

3) +3 − -7 = -4   4) -6 − -2 = +4

5) +1 − +4 = +3   6) +4 + -7 = −3

Remember: digits with no signs are positive.

7) -2 − +3 = −1   8) -4 + +9 = −5   10

9) +1 − -6 = − 5   10) + 6 + +9 = +15

d. Multiplying and Dividing

The following rules also apply for **Multiplying & Dividing**:
When signs are the **same** the result is always **positive** (+).
When signs are **different** the result is always **negative** (−).

+	×	−	⟶	−		+	÷	−	⟶	−
−	×	+	⟶	−		−	÷	+	⟶	−
+	×	+	⟶	+		+	÷	+	⟶	+
−	×	−	⟶	+		−	÷	−	⟶	+

Example: Show directed number combinations of **2, 3 & 6**.

+2 × -3 is	2 × -3 = -6	+6 ÷ -3 is 6 ÷ -3 = -2
-2 × +3 is	-2 × 3 = -6	-6 ÷ +3 is -6 ÷ 3 = -2
+2 × +3 is	2 × 3 = 6	+6 ÷ +3 is 6 ÷ 3 = 2
-2 × -3 is	2 × 3 = 6	-6 ÷ -3 is 6 ÷ 3 = 2

Exercise 19: 3 Calculate the following: Score 10

1) -4 × -3 = 12   2) +9 ÷ -3 = −3

3) -8 ÷ -2 = 4   4) +9 × -5 = −45

5) +7 × +3 = 21   6) +4 ÷ -2 = −2

7) 6 × 9 = 54   8) -12 ÷ 6 = −2

9) -16 ÷ 4 = −4   10) -8 × 7 = −56

2. Order of Operations
a. Brackets for Separation

Brackets ( ) are used (in pairs) to enclose an operation that is to be treated as one complete quantity and evaluated first.

Example: Show $2 \times 5 + 4$ with brackets and solve the sum.

$(2 \times 5) + 4 \longrightarrow$ The bracket is done first and then the addition. $\quad 10 + 4 = 14$

Brackets are used to indicate the **Order of Operations**. Multiplications and divisions are often bracketed to show that they must be completed first.

Example: Show $6 \times 3 + 4 \times 5$ in a bracketed form.

$$(6 \times 3) + (4 \times 5) = 18 + 20 = 38$$

Ignoring the brackets will lead to an incorrect order of operations and totally wrong answers.

$6 \times 3 + 4 \times 5 = 18 + 4 \times 5 = 22 \times 5 = 110$ (wrong)

Exercise 19: 4 Calculate the following:

1) $(-5 \times 7) - 4 = \underline{-39}$ ✓ (−35)

2) $(6 \times 9) + 9 = \underline{63}$ ✓

3) $8 + (-5 \div -2) = $ ✓ (−3)

4) $(4 \div -2) \times 3 = \underline{-6}$ ✓ (−2)

5) $(-4 \times -2) + 10 = \underline{18}$ ✓ (8)

6) $(-2 + 9) - 8 = \underline{-1}$ ✓ (7)

7) $(-12 \div -3) \times (-8 \times 7) = \underline{-224}$ ✓ (−4) (−56)

8) $(-8 + 4) + (16 \div -4) = \underline{-16}$ ✓ (−12) (−4)

9) $(-16 \div 4) + (3 \times 2) = \underline{2}$ ✓ (−4) (+6)

10) $(-8 \div -2) \div (4 - 2) = \underline{2}$ ✓ (4) (2)

Score $\boxed{10}$

b. The Associative Rule

A group of quantities connected by repeated operators will give the same result if their order stays the same. It will not matter how they are grouped (bracketed).

Example: Demonstrate the associative rule with $3 \times 4 \times 5$.

$$(5 \times 3) \times 4 = 60 \longrightarrow 3 \times (4 \times 5) = 60$$

The numbers **3**, **4** and **5** in this multiplication can be paired (bracketed) in different ways but will always give the answer **60**. The operation is associative.

Example: Show the associative rule with **8**, **4** and **2**.

$$(8 + 4) + 2 = 14 \longrightarrow 8 + (4 + 2) = 14$$
$$(8 \times 4) \times 2 = 64 \longrightarrow 8 \times (4 \times 2) = 64$$

Addition and multiplication are associative.

$$(8 \div 4) \div 2 = 1 \longrightarrow 8 \div (4 \div 2) = 4$$
$$(8 - 4) - 2 = 2 \longrightarrow 8 - (4 - 2) = 6$$

Subtraction and division are **not** associative.

c. The Distributive Rule

The **Distributive Rule** of arithmetic states that multiplication is distributed over addition.

Example: Demonstrate the distributive rule with $2 \times (3 + 5)$

$$2 \times (3 + 5) \longrightarrow 6 + 10 = 16$$
$$(2 \times 3) + (2 \times 5)$$

The **3** and the **5** within the bracket are multiplied by the **2** outside the bracket.

A minus sign in front of a bracket means 'multiply by **-1**'.

Example: Demonstrate the distributive rule with $-(5 - 3)$

$$-(5 - 3) = -5 + 3 = -2$$

Remember:
Minus × Minus = Plus

d. Brackets for Multiplication

If two numbers are multiplied by the same number the standard way of representing it is with two brackets.

Example: | Show $4 \times 3 + 4 \times 5$ in bracketed form.

$$(4 \times 3) + (4 \times 5)$$

This type of bracketed expression can be shown more simply by using only one bracket. **Everything inside the bracket is multiplied by everything outside the bracket.**

Example: | Show $(4 \times 3) + (4 \times 5)$ with one bracket only.

$$4(3 + 5)$$

The distributive rule is applied here - multiplication is distributed over addition (multiplication is applied to each of the added numbers in the bracket). The bracket is **expanded** or **solved** by multiplying out the numbers.

Example: | Expand or solve the sum $4(3 + 5)$

$(4 \times 3) + (4 \times 5)$
$$12 + 20 = 32$$

If the number outside the bracket is negative, all the signs of the terms inside the bracket are changed.

Example: | Expand the sum $-2(4 + 5)$

$(\text{-}2 \times 4) + (\text{-}2 \times 5)$
$$\text{-}8 - 10 = \text{-}18$$

Brackets can result in squared numbers.

Example: | Expand the sum $3(3 + 4)$

$$3^2 + 12 = 9 + 12$$
$(3 \times 3) + (3 \times 4)$
$$= 21$$

A squared bracket means all its contents are squared.

Example: | Expand the sum $(1 + 4)^2$

$$(5)^2 = 5 \times 5$$
$$= 25$$

A squared negative number always gives a positive answer.

Example: | Expand the sum $(1 - 6)^2$ |

$$(-5)^2 = -5 \times -5 = 25$$

Exercise 19: 5 Put these sums into single brackets:

Score

1) -3×-3

= _9_

2) $(2 \times 3) + (2 \times 4)$

= _14_

3) $(5 \times -3) + (5 \times 7)$

= _____

4) $4^2 + 20$

= _____

Expand then solve the bracketed expressions:

5) $3(3 - -5) = 3 \times (3 - -5)$ = _24_

6) $-3(5 + 2) = -3 \times (5 + 2)$ = _21_

7) $-7(-5 + -2) = -7 \times (-5 + -2)$ = _-49_

Give the solutions to these bracketed sums:

8) $5(5 - 3)$

= _10_

9) $(5 + 2)^2$

= _49_

10) $6(3 + 6)$

= _54_

e. BIDMAS (BODMAS)

BIDMAS is an acronym which helps to remind us of the order certain operations have to follow:

B I D M A S

Brackets, **I**ndices, **D**ivide, **M**ultiply, **A**dd, **S**ubtract

Order of Operations is as follows:

1. Do anything in **Brackets**.
2. Do anything with **Indices** (or powers).
3. Do any **Dividing** or **Multiplying** (in the order of the question).
4. Do any **Adding** or **Subtracting** (in the order of the question).

Example: Work out the following sum using BIDMAS:

$$\frac{30}{(4+2)} \times (1 + 2 \times 3)^2 - 4$$

1.a. Work out the brackets first:
$(4 + 2) = 6$

b. BIDMAS applies within the brackets. Multiply, add and then square:
$(1 + 2 \times 3)^2$
$2 \times 3 = 6 + 1 = 7^2 = 49$

$$\frac{30}{6} \times 49 - 4$$

$$5 \times 49 - 4$$

2. Next work out the division and then the multiplication:
$30 \div 6 = 5; \quad 5 \times 49 = 245$

$$245 - 4$$

$$241 \text{ (answer)}$$

3. Now do the subtraction:
$245 - 4 = 241$

Exercise 19: 6   Calculate the following: Score

The two sums are treated as bracketed.

1) $(22 - 3) \times (5 + 4)$

$= \underline{17}$

2) $\dfrac{50 - 2}{-4 \times 2} \longrightarrow \dfrac{(50 - 2)}{(-4 \times 2)}$

$= \underline{}$

3) $(10 \times 12) + (2 \times \text{-}5)^2$

$= \underline{}$

4) $2(2 + \text{-}3) + 2$

$= \underline{}$

5) $(3 \times 6) + (\text{-}1 \times \text{-}5) + (3 \times 1)^2 = \underline{}$

6) $\text{-}4(\text{-}5 + 2) - 6$

$= \underline{}$

7) $(7^2 + 2^2) - (4 - 1)^2$

$= \underline{}$

8) $4(\text{-}2 - 2) + (\text{-}3 - 5) + (3 \times 2)^2 = \underline{}$

9) $\dfrac{(3 \times \text{-}5)}{(6 - 9)} + 10 = \underline{}$

10) $20 - 5(\text{-}3 + 2)$

$= \underline{}$

3. Arithmetic Equations

Equations are mathematical sentences or number sentences that always follow the same pattern. What is on the left side is **balanced** or **equal to** what is on the right side. This is always signified by an **equals sign**.

Examples: Show equations using the four rules of number.

Both equations remain balanced giving the same answer on each side.

$$7 - 3 = 1 + 3 \qquad 2 \times 3 = 12 \div 2$$
$$4 = 4 \qquad\qquad 6 = 6$$

a. Missing Numbers

The equals sign permits a **Missing Number** to be found. Inverse operations can be used to solve the equations. Remember: + is the inverse of − and × is the inverse of ÷

Examples: Find the missing numbers in these equations:

$$\boxed{?} + 6 = 13$$

The number in the box is **7** because:
$\boxed{7} + 6 = 13$ (inverted $\boxed{7} = 13 - 6$)

$$6 \times \boxed{?} = 18$$

The number in the box is **3** because:
$6 \times \boxed{3} = 18$ (inverted $\boxed{3} = 18 \div 6$)

Exercise 19: 7a   Calculate the following:

1) $50 - \boxed{} = 31$

2) $76 + 35 = 82 + \boxed{}$

3) $(56 \div 7) - 4 = \boxed{} - 24$

4) $\boxed{} + 5 = 26$

5) $(\text{-}5 \times \text{-}7) + 9 = (36 \div \boxed{}) + 40$

6) $129 - 50 = \boxed{} - 6$

7) $\boxed{} + 16 = 39 + 8$

8) $(12 \times \text{-}7) + 83 = (8 \times 10) - \boxed{}$

Arithmetic equations can sometimes be in problem form.

Example: | What must you multiply **2** by to get an answer which is **half** of **12**?

$$2 \times \boxed{?} = 12 \div 2 \quad \text{(half of 12)}$$

$$6 = 6$$

Answer is **3**

Exercise 19: 7b Calculate the following:

9) What must you multiply **30** by to get an answer that is **half** of **300**? _____

10) What must be added to **63** so that it will equal **5** groups of **15**? _____

Score

b. Missing Signs

The equals sign permits a **Missing Sign** to be found. Test different signs to find the correct operation.

Example: | Find the missing operation in this equation:

$$9 \boxed{?} 5 = 14$$

The operation in the box is + because:

$$9 \boxed{+} 5 = 14$$

(Check it with the inverse operations.)

$$14 - 5 = 9$$
$$14 - 9 = 5$$

Exercise 19: 8 Calculate the following:

1) $40 \boxed{} 9 = 31$ 2) $13 + 35 = 12 \boxed{} 4$

3) $(32 \div 4) - 4 = 28 \boxed{} 24$ 4) $57 \boxed{} 3 = 19$

5) $12 \times 6 = 96 \boxed{} 24$ 6) $3 \times 17 = 100 \boxed{} 49$

7) $33 - 17 = 4 \boxed{} 12$ 8) $21 \div 3 = 84 \boxed{} 12$

9) $5(5 + 3) + 100 = 100 + 30 + (40 \boxed{} 4)$

10) $(6 \times 3) \boxed{} 6 = 13 + 43 + 63 - 11$

Score

4. Function Machines

Function Machines (also known as Number Machines or Mappings - see Maths Workbook 5) are equations.

Example: | How do function machines relate to equations?

Input Value	**Operations**	**Output Value**
(a number goes	(add, subtract,	(a number comes
into the machine)	multiply, divide)	out of the machine)

Any input value can be placed in the function machine.

IN   **OPERATION**   **OUT**

$$36 \Rightarrow \boxed{\div\ 3} \Rightarrow 12$$

$$36 \div 3 = 12$$

The output value is equal to the input value with the operational process acting on it. This means the function machine can be viewed as an equation.

a. Finding Output Values

Output Values are discovered by applying the order of operations in which they appear in the function machine.

Example: | Find the output value of the machine.

IN   **OPERATION**   **OUT**

$$6 \Rightarrow \boxed{\times\ 2\ +\ 4} \Rightarrow \underline{\ ?\ }$$

Multiply by **2** and add **4**

This machine has more than one operation:

$6 \times 2 = 12$ $12 + 4 = 16$

The output value = 16

Tables can show the results of a function machine. Different amounts can be fed into the same function machine with the following results:

In	Out
12 ——→	28
16 ——→	36
20 ——→	44
24 ——→	52

Exercise 19: 9 Calculate the following: Score

1) $24 \rightarrow \boxed{\div 3} \rightarrow \underline{}$ 2) $3 \rightarrow \boxed{\times 9 - 7} \rightarrow \underline{}$

3) $57 \rightarrow \boxed{\div 3 - {-7}} \rightarrow \underline{}$ 4) $33 \rightarrow \boxed{\times 5} \rightarrow \underline{}$

Fill in the function machine before calculating:

5) $20 \rightarrow \boxed{} \rightarrow \underline{}$ 6) $11 \rightarrow \boxed{} \rightarrow \underline{}$

   Multiply by **9** and subtract **18**.   Add **15** and divide by **2**.

7) $8 \rightarrow \boxed{- 3 \times 13} \rightarrow \underline{}$

8-10) Use the operations $- 3 \times 13$ in this
      function machine to calculate the
      three output values in the table:

In	Out
-4	——
6	——
11	——

b. Finding Input Values

Input Values are found by using inverse operations:

> Add ⟷ Subtract ¦ Multiply ⟷ Divide

Example: Find the input value of the machine.

IN	OPERATION	OUT

$\underline{?} \rightarrow \boxed{\times 3 + 8} \rightarrow 20$

← ——————— Go backwards

Invert the operations:
Change divide to multiply.
Change add to subtract.

$20 - 8$	$12 \div 3$
$= 12$	$= 4$
Subtract **8**	Divide by **3**

The input value = **4**

The table shows more input values found by inverse operations.

In	Out
7 ←	29
6 ←	26
5 ←	23
2 ←	14

Exercise 19: 10 Calculate the following:

1) ___ →| $\div 5$ |→ **75**   2) ___ →| $\times 9 + 9$ |→ **90**

3) ___ →| $\times 3 + 3$ |→ **63**   4) ___ →| $\times 4$ |→ **96**

Fill in the function machine before calculating:

5) ___ →| |→ **76**   6) ___ →| |→ **91**

    Multiply by **4** and add **20**.   Multiply by **5** and add **16**.

7) ___ →| $- 2 \times 11$ |→ **44**

8-10) Use the operations $- 2 \times 11$ in this function machine to calculate the input values in the table:

In	Out
___	66
___	88
___	132

c. Finding Number Operations

A missing operation is found by guessing and testing.
Try the operations $+ - \times \div$ in the function machine:

Example: | Find the missing operation in the machine. |

- As the number is increasing we do not divide or subtract.
- We cannot multiply since there is no multiple that will increase **54** to **99**.
- We must add. The answer can be found by inverting the operation to subtract.

IN   OPERATION   OUT

9 →| $\times 6$ | **?** |→ **99**

Multiply by **6** and **?**

Calculate the first operation. $9 \times 6 = 54$

To find the add, invert and subtract. $99 - 54 = 45$
$54\boxed{+ 45} = 99$

The missing operation is: **Add 45**

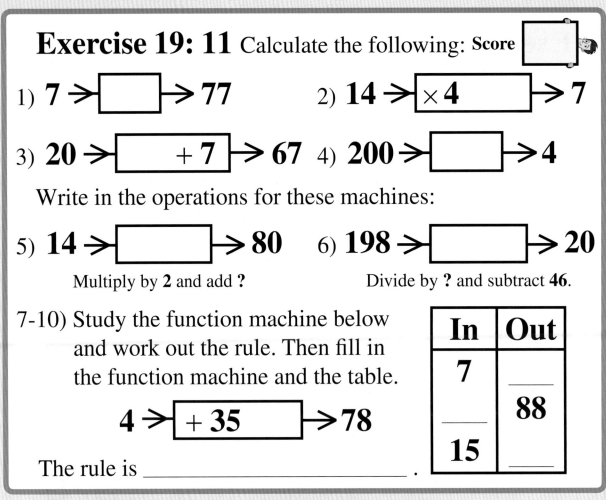

Exercise 19: 11 Calculate the following: **Score** [ ]

1) $7 \rightarrow \boxed{} \rightarrow 77$
2) $14 \rightarrow \boxed{\times 4} \rightarrow 7$

3) $20 \rightarrow \boxed{ + 7} \rightarrow 67$
4) $200 \rightarrow \boxed{} \rightarrow 4$

Write in the operations for these machines:

5) $14 \rightarrow \boxed{} \rightarrow 80$
6) $198 \rightarrow \boxed{} \rightarrow 20$

Multiply by **2** and add **?**   Divide by **?** and subtract **46**.

7-10) Study the function machine below and work out the rule. Then fill in the function machine and the table.

$$4 \rightarrow \boxed{+ 35} \rightarrow 78$$

In	Out
7	___
___	88
15	___

The rule is _____ .

5. What is Algebra?

In **Algebra** letters or symbols called **Variables** represent missing numbers. Italicised lower case (small) letters are normally used from the beginning or end of the alphabet. A same capital and lower case letter represent different amounts.

The letters mostly used in algebra are:

$$a, b, c \text{ and } x, y, z$$

A **Constant** is a value that remains unchanged. It is usually a number. **Terms** are quantities (constants and/or variables) that are linked by + or − signs.

Variable $\longrightarrow x + 6 \longleftarrow$ **Constant**

The variable and constant are terms because they are linked by a + sign.

A **Coefficient** is a constant that is associated or connected with a variable. It stands in front of the variable. The value of the variable is multiplied by the coefficient.

$$\text{Coefficient} \longrightarrow 2x \longleftarrow \text{Variable}$$

$2x$ is really $2 \times x$ Now assume $x = 5$

The variable **5** is multiplied by the coefficient of $\times$ **2**.

$$2x \longrightarrow 2 \times 5 = 10$$

If a variable has a coefficient of **1**, it does not have to be included, i.e. $1x = x$

An **Expression** is a collection of quantities made up of constants and variables linked by operation signs such as $+$ and $-$. It does not include an equals sign.

All expressions with two or more terms are **Multinomial** or **Polynomial**.

A multinomial expression with just two terms is **Binomial**. A multinomial expression with three terms is **Trinomial**.

$$x + y \qquad\qquad 3 + x^2 - y \qquad\qquad 4(x - y)$$

Binomial   **Trinomial**   **Binomial**

'Like Terms' are those terms that are completely identical in respect to their variables and powers. Their coefficients, however, can be different.

'Like Terms' $\longrightarrow$ $2x$ and x $3y^2$ and $2y^2$

Same variables, coefficients can be different.   Same variables and powers, coefficients can be different.

'Unlike Terms' $\longrightarrow$ x and y $4y$ and $3y^2$

Different variables.   Same variables but powers must be the same.

An **Algebraic Equation** is a mathematical statement where two expressions (one can be a constant) have equal value.

Binomial Expression ⟶ $2x + 7 = \underline{\underline{15}}$ ⟵ **Expression (constant only)**

Binomial Expression ⟶ $\boxed{2\overset{x}{x} \overset{75}{+} 5} = \underline{x + 14 - 4}$ ⟵ **Trinomial Expression**

$2 + {}^{14} - {}_{-y}$

Exercise 19: 12 Answer the following:

Which of these terms:

$$x + \textcircled{5} - 3y$$
$? + 5 - 3y$

1) are constants? __5__

2) contain variables? x & $3y$

3) show coefficients? __3y__

4) Is the expression binomial or trinomial? __trinomial__

Write whether these terms are like or unlike:

5) **2x** and **9** __un__   6) **5x** and **4y** __un__ 7) x and **3x** __like__

8) x^2 and **2x** __un__ 9) x and y __un__ 10) $2q^2$ and $4a^2$ __like__

---

6. Algebraic Operations
a. Simplifying Algebraic Expressions

Directed number rules and BIDMAS apply to algebraic expressions. To **Simplify Expressions** we add, subtract, multiply or divide the like terms.

b. Adding and Subtracting Terms

Expressions are simplified by **Combining** or **Collecting** (adding or subtracting) the like terms.

Example 1: | Add or subtract terms with single variables.

Like terms can be added or subtracted. Note that *p* means **1p**.

$$3p + p = 4p$$

Example 2: | Add or subtract terms with multiple variables.

Note that **xy** is the same as **yx**. The simplified expression puts the letters in alphabetical order.

$$7xy - 3yx = 4xy$$

Example 3: | Add and subtract a number of terms.

Collect all the like terms (separate *y* and *x* terms and number only terms).

Add and subtract the separate terms.

$$3x + x + 4y - 2x - y + 2y$$
$$= 3x + x - 2x + 4y + 2y - y$$
$$= 2x + 5y$$

Exercise 19: 13 Simplify the following: Score

1) $7x + 7 - x + 1$

$= \underline{7x - x + 7 + 1} = \underline{6x + 8}$

2) $8y - 3z - 2y + -2z$

$= \underline{\hspace{2cm}} = \underline{\hspace{1cm}}$

3) $4y - 4z - -2y + 9$

$= \underline{4y - -2y + 9 -} = \underline{6y - 4z = 9}$
     $\underset{6}{\underbrace{\hspace{1cm}}} \overset{-}{\underset{9}{}}$

4) $2a - 4a - b + 8b$

$= \underline{\hspace{2cm}} = \underline{\hspace{1cm}}$

5) $yz + 2zy - x + 2x$

$= \underline{\hspace{2cm}} = \underline{\hspace{1cm}}$

6) $-y - 2y + y + z - 5y$

$= \underline{\hspace{2cm}} = \underline{\hspace{1cm}}$

7) $5xyz + 2xy - 4zyx$

$= \underline{\hspace{2cm}} = \underline{\hspace{1cm}}$

8) $4c - 3a - 2b + 5a$

$= \underline{\hspace{2cm}} = \underline{\hspace{1cm}}$

9) $-x + 5x - x + 4y + y = \underline{\hspace{2cm}} = \underline{\hspace{1cm}}$

10) $y - 3y - 2y + 3z + x = \underline{\hspace{2cm}} = \underline{\hspace{1cm}}$

c. Multiplying and Dividing Terms

Expressions can be simplified by **Multiplying** or **Dividing** 'like quantities within terms'. The rules are as follows:

Example 1: | Multiply two variables together. |

Leave out the multiplication sign and place the two variables next to each other.

$$x \times y = xy$$

Example 2: | Multiply two variables with coefficients. |

Multiply the coefficients together and place the variables next to each other.

$$5x \times 3y = 15xy$$

Example 3: | Multiply two/three variables that are the same. |

Write the variable and square it.

$$x \times x = x^2$$

Squared negative terms become positive.

$$^-x \times ^-x = x^2$$

Variables can be cubed too.

$$x \times x \times x = x^3$$

Example 4: | Multiply two same variables with coefficients. |

Multiply the two coefficients together and square the variable.

$$3y \times 4y = 12y^2$$

Example 5: | Multiply two same and one different variable. |

Square the same variables, then multiply with the different variable.

$$y \times x \times x = x^2y$$

Example 6: | Divide two variables. |

Write the variables in the form of a fraction.

$$x \div y = \frac{x}{y}$$

An expression simplifies just like any other fraction:

$$\frac{\cancel{2}x}{\cancel{2}y} = \frac{x}{y}$$

Score

Exercise 19: 14   Simplify the following:

1) $5x \times ^-7$

= _____

2) $y \times yx$

= _____

3) $5x \div y =$ _____

4) $\dfrac{10y}{5} =$ _____

5) $y \times 7xy =$ _____

6) $y \times y \times y =$ _____

7) $5x \times 5x \times y \div 4 =$ _____

8) $24x \div {\text-}6 =$ _____

9) $2a \times b \times b =$ _____

10) $2z \times 4x \times 3y =$ _____

d. Brackets and Expansion

All the previous rules for brackets apply. Any digit or variable outside a bracket multiplies (**expands**) each term separately inside the bracket (distributive rule):

Example 1: | Expand the brackets: $2(a + b)$ |

$$2(a + b) \longrightarrow (2 \times a) + (2 \times b) \longrightarrow 2a + 2b$$

With more complex expressions expand the brackets and then collect the like terms.

Example 2: | Expand the brackets: $2(x - 1) + 3(x + y)$ |

$$2(x - 1) + 3(x + y)$$
$$2x - 2 + 3x + 3y$$
$$5x + 3y - 2$$

Negative terms outside a bracket change all the signs within the bracket.

Expressions can be put in a single bracket by dividing the terms by the same variable and/or constant which then goes outside the bracket.

Example 3: | Put into single brackets: $4ab + 8b$ |

Divide both terms by $4b$

$$\longrightarrow 4b(a + 2)$$

Exercise 19: 15 Multiply out the brackets:

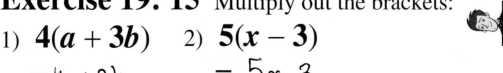

Score

1) $4(a + 3b)$

$= 4a + 3b$

2) $5(x - 3)$

$= 5x - 3$

3) $6(2x + y)$

$= 6 2x + y$

4) $3p(4p + 3q)$

$= 3p \times 4p + 3q$

5) $2(3a + 4b)$

$= 2 3a + 4b$

Multiply out the brackets, then collect like terms:

6) $3(a + 2) + 2(a + b)$ 7) $4(a - b) - 3(a + b)$

= _____   = _____

= _____   = _____

Put the following expressions into single brackets:

8) $3a^2 - 2ab$ 9) $ab - a^2$ 10) $9xy + 6xz$

= _____   = _____   = _____

e. Brackets (Addition/Subtraction)

When adding and subtracting, brackets can be used to clarify the calculations necessary.

Example 1: Find the sum of $x + 2y$, $4x - y$ and $y - x$

1. Bracket the sums. $(x + 2y) + (4x - y) + (y - x)$

2. Collect the terms. $x + 4x - x + 2y - y + y$

3. Simplify. $4x + 2y$

Some questions must be read carefully to avoid confusion.

Example 2: To what must $2x - y$ be added to give $5y + 3x$?

1. Bracket and set out. $(5y + 3x) - (2x - y)$

2. Multiply out. $5y + 3x - 2x + y$ →

3. Collect the terms. $5y + y + 3x - 2x$

4. Simplify. $6y + x$

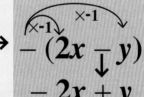

$$- (2x - y)$$
$$- 2x + y$$

Note: **Minus $\times$ Minus = Plus**

Exercise 19: 16   Calculate the following:

Score

1) Subtract $5x - 3y$ from $x + 2y$. _____

2) Add together $x + y$, $2x - y$ and $3x + 4y$. _____

3) What do we add to $y + 2z$ to give $5y + 9z$?

Write as $(5y + 9z) - (y + 2z) = 5y + 9z - y - 2z = $ _____

4) Subtract $2a - 3b$ from b. _____

5) Subtract $a - 2b$ from $3a + b$. _____

6) To what must $5x + 3$ be added to give $3 + 6x$? _____

7) What must be taken away from x to leave 11? _____

8) Subtract $3x + 7y - 7$ from $8y + 3x$. _____

9) Find the total of $8y + 3$, $2 - y$ and -8. _____

10) From $4x - 3y - z$ subtract $3x - y + z$. _____

7. Substitution

Replacing a variable (letter) with a number is called **Substitution**. Substitute the given values for the letters. Expressions are calculated using the order of operations.

Example: | If $x = 4$ work out the value of $3(x - 2)$. |

$\boxed{x = 4}$ $3(x - 2)$ Substitute 4 for x ⟶ $3(4 - 2)$

$$= 3 \times 2 = 6$$

Exercise 19: 17 Find the value of these expressions:

| If $x = 5$; $y = 3$; $z = 2$ |

1) $(5x + 3y) - z$

$\begin{array}{r} 125 \\ +\ 9 \\ \hline 134 \end{array}$

$25^5 + 9 - 2$

$= \underline{32}$

2) xyz

$= $ _____

3) $x(x + 2) + 2z$

$= $ _____

4) $-3(2y + z) + yz$

$= $ _____

5) $8(x - y) - z$

$= $ _____

23

$$\boxed{\text{If } a = 6; \; b = \text{-}4; \; c = 2}$$

6) $\dfrac{a + c}{b} = \underline{}$

7) $3a - 2b = \underline{}$

8) $5(c + b) = \underline{}$

9) $3a + c^3 - b = \underline{}$

10) $\dfrac{a^2 + b^2 + 8}{c(2 + 4)} = \underline{}$

8. More Number Sequences

A **Sequence** is a set of numbers or objects made or written in order, according to a mathematical rule. (See Maths Workbook 1 for introductory work on Number Sequences.) Each value in the sequence is called a term. It is algebra because there are **missing terms** (usually denoted by **n**).

a. Using the Gaps

There is an operational relationship between the numbers. The Four Rules of Number $+ - \times \div$ give the basis for solving all sequences. Look for what is happening in the gaps between the numbers.

Example: | What is the rule for this number sequence? |

1   3   5   7   9   The next term is: **11**
   2   2   2   2   The rule is: **Add 2**

1. Numbers may leapfrog over each other and create two sequences, e.g. **2, 1, 4, 2, 6, 3, 8, 4**   (2, 4, 6, 8)
                                                           (1, 2, 3, 4)

2. A quick guide to operations:

> **Adding** - numbers get **bigger slowly**
> **Multiplying** - numbers get **bigger quickly**
> **Subtracting** - numbers get **smaller slowly**
> **Dividing** - numbers get **smaller quickly**

Note: The multiplying and dividing guides do not apply to fractions (or decimals) which are smaller than 1.

b. Common Number Patterns

Familiarity with certain sequence types can save time. The most common types of sequences are:

Arithmetic Progression - Each new term is made by adding a constant amount to the previous term.

1, 4, 7, 10, 13, 16 Add 3 - next term is **19**

Geometric Progression - Each new term is made by multiplying the previous term by a constant amount.

1, 4, 16, 64 Times by 4 - next term is **256**

Doubling Sequence - Each new term is twice the value of the previous term.

1, 2, 4, 8, 16 Times by 2 - next term is **32**

Fibonacci Sequence - Each new term is made by adding together the previous two terms starting at 1, 1 .

1, 1, 2, 3, 5, 8 Add two previous terms - next term is **13**

Lucas Sequence - Each new term is made by adding together the previous two terms starting at 1, 3 .

1, 3, 4, 7, 11, 18 Add two previous terms - next term is **29**

Alternating Sequence - Terms are alternately positive and negative. **1, -1, 2, -2, 3, -3** Next term is **4**

Square Numbers (*n*th term is n^2)   **1, 4, 9, 16, 25**

Cube Numbers (*n*th term is n^3) **1, 8, 27, 64, 125**

Triangular Numbers   **1, 3, 6, 10, 15, 21**

Rectangular Numbers **4, 6, 8, 9, 10, 12**

Prime Numbers   **2, 3, 5, 7, 11, 13, 17**

1) **21,   15,   10,   6,** ___ , ___   2) **1, 5, 25, 125,** ___ , ___

3) **10,   12,   14,   15,** ___ , ___   4) **0, -1, -3, -6,** ___ , ___

5) **7,   11,   18,   29,** ___ , ___   6) **5, 7, 11, 13,** ___ , ___

7) **80, 40, 20, 10,** ___ , ___   8) **1, 4, 9, 16,** ___ , ___

9) **1, 2, 6, 24, 120 ,** ___   10) **216, 125, 64,** ___ , ___

9. Finding the nth Term
a. Arithmetic Progressions
(i) The Inductive Rule

Arithmetic Progressions follow the **Inductive Rule** (the previous term is used as a basis for finding the next term). These progressions have equal spacing between terms.

Example: | Find the **n**th term through the inductive rule.

$$4 \searrow_6 \nearrow 10 \searrow_6 \nearrow 16 \searrow_6 \nearrow 22 \searrow_6 \nearrow 28 \quad \_\_\_$$

The pattern adds **6** - the next term is: **28 + 6 = 34**

The **10th** term can be worked out by counting forward.

$$28 + 6 + 6 + 6 + 6 + 6 = 58$$
← **5th** term + **5** more **6s**   ← **10th** term

It is not practical to count forward to the **100th** term.
The **100th** term is **95** terms more than the **5th** term:

$$28 + (95 \times 6) = 598$$

The above term is **28** + (**95** terms more × gap of **6**) = **100th** term is **598**

Exercise 19: 19a Find the **n**th term by induction:

1) **6,   11,   16,   21,   26** a) **13th** term ___ b) **19th** term ___

2) **3,   10,   17,   24,   31** a) **15th** term ___ b) **23rd** term ___

(ii) The Difference Method

The **Difference Method** does not use the previous term (not inductive). Only the **term number** is required (this is the term we wish to find, e.g. **14th** term). An algebraic rule will apply to all terms that follow this particular pattern.

Example: | Find the **nth** term by the difference method. |

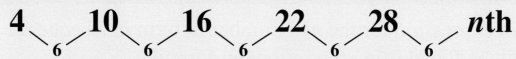

1. What is the gap between each number? It is **6**.

2. It is therefore related to the **6** times table.

3. It is the **6** times table shifted **two** places to the left for this particular sequence.

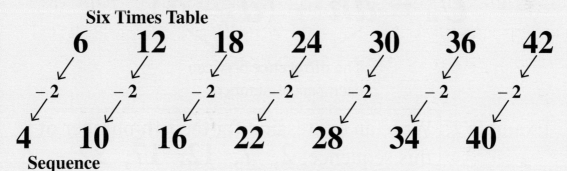

Six Times Table

Sequence

The Algebraic Rule

The **nth** number is multiplied by the gap of **6**.

It is expressed **6n**

The original number pattern is 2 less than the **6** times table.

It is expressed as **− 2**

The rule is: $6n - 2$

The **10th** term will be: $6 \times 10 - 2 = 58$

The **100th** term will be: $6 \times 100 - 2 = 598$

Exercise 19: 19b Find using the difference method:

3) a) **3, 5, 7, 9, 11** Algebraic rule: _____

   b) What is the: **14th** term? _____ **19th** term? _____

4) a) **3, 7, 11, 15, 19** Algebraic rule: _____

   b) What is the: **15th** term? _____ **32nd** term? _____

5) a) **6, 11, 16, 21, 26** Algebraic rule: _____

   b) What is the: **12th** term? _____ **16th** term? _____

(iii) Using the Formula

An expression for the **nth** number or term in a sequence can be found using the following formula:

The **nth term** is usually expressed as U_n (Unknown Number)

The **nth term** we need to find.

The **first number** in the sequence.

$$U_n = dn + (a - d)$$

The **difference** between each pair of numbers.

Example 1: | Write an expression for the **nth** number of this sequence: **2, 7, 12, 17, 22**

$U_n = dn + (a - d)$

$U_n = 5n + (2 - 5)$

$U_n = 5n - 3$

• The first number is **2**.
• The difference between each pair of numbers is **5**.
This is an expression for the **nth** number of this sequence.

Example 2: | Find the **15th** number of the same sequence: **2, 7, 12, 17, 22**

$U_{15} = 5n - 3 \longrightarrow$

Substitution

This is the **15th** number of this sequence.

$U_{15} = 5 \times 15 - 3$

$U_{15} = 75 - 3$

$U_{15} = 72$

Exercise 19: 19c Find using the formula:

6) a) **7, 12, 17, 22, 27** Algebraic rule: $U_n =$ _____

   b) The **18th** term is? $U_{18} =$ ___ **29th** term? $U_{29} =$ ___

7) a) **5, 11, 17, 23, 29** Algebraic rule: $U_n =$ _____

   b) The **16th** term is? $U_{16} =$ ___ **38th** term is? $U_{38} =$ ___

Study the match patterns. Write down an algebraic rule for the ***n*th** pattern using ***m*** for matches. Then find the number of matches required in each case for the pattern:

8) a) Rule: $m =$ _____   b) **15th** pattern: ___ matches

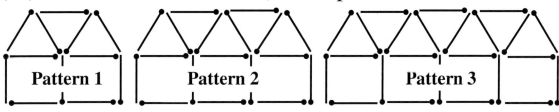

Pattern 1   Pattern 2   Pattern 3

9) a) Rule: $m =$ _____

   b) **23rd** pattern:

      ___ matches

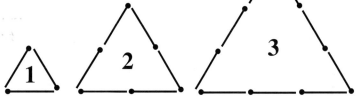

10) a) Rule: $m =$ _____   b) **15th** pattern: ___ matches

  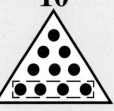

b. Triangle Number Progressions

Triangular Numbers are sequenced as follows:	1	3	6	10
	Start with 1	Add 2	Add 3	Add 4

For the **fifth** triangular number add **5** and so on.

1 $^{+2}$ **3** $^{+3}$ **6** $^{+4}$ **10** $^{+5}$ **15** $^{+6}$ etc.

The **nth** triangular number is given by:

$$n(n + 1) \div 2$$

Example: | What is the **10th** (**nth**) triangular number?

Substitute **10** for **n** to find the **nth** number.

$n(n + 1) \div 2$

$10(10 + 1) \div 2$

The **10th** triangular number is **55**.

$10(11) \div 2$

$110 \div 2$

Exercise 19: 20a   Answer the following:

1) What is the **13th** triangular number?

$n(n + 1) \div 2$ $13(13 + 1) \div 2$ $13(14) \div 2$ $182 \div 2$

The **13th** triangular number is ___.

Find the **nth** triangular number.

2) **17th**: 103   3) **27th**: _____   4) **22nd**: _____

5) **18th**: _____   6) **24th**: _____   7) **29th**: _____

8) **40th**: _____

c. Triangle Number Problems

Triangle number progressions can be used to solve different types of mathematical problems.

Example: | A football competition was held between **five** year 6 five-a-side teams. Each team played every other team once. How many games did the teams play in total?

One way of solving this problem is to write out each game in turn as follows:

The five teams could be labelled: **A B C D E**

Start with team A's games, then move to B's games, etc.

A versus B;	**B versus C**;	**C versus D**;
A versus C;	**B versus D**;	**C versus E**;
A versus D;	**B versus E**;	
A versus E;		**D versus E**;

Answer: There are **10** games played altogether.

The problem can also be solved using triangle number progressions:

There are **5** teams and this corresponds to the **4th** triangular number. As the **4th** triangular number is **10** it means there are **10** games in total.

The answer can also be found using a formula:

The **nth** triangular number is found by: $n(n + 1) \div 2$. This formula can be adjusted to: $n(n - 1) \div 2$. Now if the **5th** triangular number is fed into the formula it will give the **4th** triangular number as the answer.

$$n(n - 1) \div 2 \longrightarrow 5(5 - 1) \div 2 \longrightarrow 20 \div 2 = 10$$

If we space out the **five** letters A to E (representing the **five** teams), lines can be drawn between them. The number of lines drawn will represent the number of matches the **five** teams played.

```
        A

E                B


    D        C
```

Join up the **five** points by drawing **five** lines. This will make a pentagon.

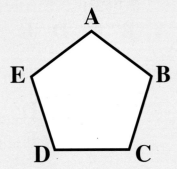

Another **five** lines can be drawn between the points. This will make a pentagram.

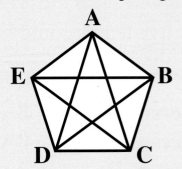

The **10** lines represent **10** matches played by the **5** teams.

Exercise 19: 20b Answer the following:

9) **Eight** basketball teams take part in a competition. Each team plays every other team once. How many games are played altogether?

   Use the formula: games played = $n(n - 1) \div 2$

   The total number of games played was _____ games.

10) **Six** athletic teams **A** to **F** race against each other. Each team races against each other separately. How many races are there in total? Join up the rest of the points to find the answer.

    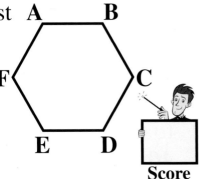

    There were _____ races in total.

    Score

10. Trial and Improvement

Sometimes a missing value (x) is found by **Trial** and **Error**. It can be a whole number or a decimal value. We find it by substituting values into an equation and testing them out.

Example: | Find the value of x in $10 - x = 4$ |

$$10 - x = 4 \longrightarrow \text{Try } x = 6 \longrightarrow 10 - 6 = 4$$

Finding the missing value **x** can often require repeated substitutions before the correct value is discovered. Some equations have **x** values on both sides adding complexity.

Example: | Find the value of x in $2x + 3 = 5 + x$

Try $x = 1$	$2x + 3 = 5 + x$	This does not balance as the **right side** is **too big**.
	$2 + 3 = 5 + 1$	
	$5 = 6$	

Try $x = 3$	$2x + 3 = 5 + x$	This does not balance as the **left side** is **too big**.
	$2 \times 3 + 3 = 5 + 3$	
	$9 = 8$	

Try $x = 2$	$2x + 3 = 5 + x$	This works as **both sides** **balance**.
	$2 \times 2 + 3 = 5 + 2$	
	$7 = 7$	

Use trial and error to find **x**.

Score

Exercise 19: 21a Choose values from the boxes to try out in the equations:

1) $3x + 5 = 2x + 8$ | 1; 2; 3; 4 | $x = $ ____

2) $5x - 4 = 5 + 2x$ | 1; 2; 3 | $x = $ ____

3) $x - 2 = 3x - 12$ | 2; 3; 4; 5 | $x = $ ____

4) $8 + 4x = 3x + 14$ | 4; 5; 6; 7 | $x = $ ____

5) $9x + 4 = 20 + 5x$ | 1; 2; 3; 4 | $x = $ ____

Finding the missing value x when it has been squared or cubed often involves working with decimals. A calculator is normally used for such calculations. Easier examples can be done on paper. (Long multiplication is often required.)

Example: | From the choices below, select the value of x which best fits the equation: $x^3 - x = 32$
$x = 3.2$ $x = 3.3$ $x = 3.4$

Try $x = 3.2$

$$(3.2)^3 - 3.2 =$$
$$(3.2 \times 3.2 \times 3.2) - 3.2 =$$
$$32.768 - 3.2 = 29.568$$

$x = 3.2$ gives a value that is too small, so try a decimal value for x which is greater than **3.2**.

Try $x = 3.4$

$$(3.4)^3 - 3.4 =$$
$$(3.4 \times 3.4 \times 3.4) - 3.4 =$$
$$39.304 - 3.4 = 35.904$$

$x = 3.4$ gives a value that is too big, so try a decimal value for x which is smaller than **3.4**.

Try $x = 3.3$

$$(3.3)^3 - 3.3 =$$
$$(3.3 \times 3.3 \times 3.3) - 3.3 =$$
$$35.937 - 3.3 = 32.637$$

$x = 3.3$ gives the closest value to **32** of the three choices. Therefore $x = 3.3$ (1 d.p.)

Exercise 19: 21b   Test the values in the boxes and choose x to 1 d.p.:

6) $x^2 = 5$ | Multiply by itself **once**:   **2.1**   **2.3**   **2.2** | $x =$ _____

7) $x^3 = 20$ | Multiply by itself **twice**:   **2.6**   **2.8**   **2.7** | $x =$ _____

8) $x^2 - x = 7$

| This equation has two terms. | 2.9 | 3 | 3.1 | 3.2 |

Test out each value and substitute it into the equation:

E.g. Try $x = 2.9$ $x^2 = 2.9 \times 2.9 = 8.41$

$x^2 - x = 7 \longrightarrow$ Substitute $\longrightarrow 8.41 - 2.9 = 5.51$ (too small)

Now try out the other values to find x: $x = $ _____

9) $x^2 + x = 5$

| 1.6 | 1.7 | 1.8 | 1.9 | $x = $ ____

10) $5x - x^2 = 5$

| 3.4 | 3.5 | 3.6 | 3.7 | $x = $ ____

11. Algebraic Equations
a. Linear Equations

A **Linear Equation** is an equation that only has **first order terms**. This means squared or cubed terms are not used. It is solved by finding the value of the missing number or variable (first order term). They can be written as arithmetic equations, function machines or as algebraic equations.

Example: | Show how a linear equation can be written. |

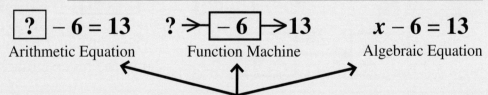

| ? | $- 6 = 13$ | ? ⇒ | -6 | ⇒13 | $x - 6 = 13$ |
| Arithmetic Equation | | Function Machine | | | Algebraic Equation |

Linear equations in an algebraic form replace the missing amount with a variable (letter) such as x or y.

Algebraic linear equations can be solved in three ways:
1) **Reverse Function Machines**.
2) **Reverse Operations**.
3) **Balancing** (doing the same thing to both sides).

b. Reverse Function Machines

Reverse Function Machines can be used algebraically.

Example: | Solve $3x - 4 = 17$ with a function machine. |

The **variable** x can be fed into a function machine to produce the equation.

IN	OPERATION	OUT

$$x \rightarrow \boxed{\times 3} \xrightarrow{3x} \boxed{-4} \rightarrow 3x - 4$$

The **constant 17** is now fed into the reverse machine to give the value of x.

$\longleftarrow$ Go backwards

$$7 \leftarrow \boxed{\div 3} \xleftarrow{21} \boxed{+4} \leftarrow 17$$

$x = 7$ satisfies the equation $3x - 4 = 17$

Exercise 19: 22a Solve the shaded equations:

1) $3y + 1 = 10$ $y \rightarrow \boxed{\times 3} \xrightarrow{3y} \boxed{+1} \rightarrow 3y + 1$

$\underline{} \leftarrow \boxed{\div 3} \xleftarrow{9} \boxed{-1} \leftarrow 10$ The constant **10** is fed into the reverse machine.

2) $\dfrac{a-2}{4} = 7$ $a \rightarrow \boxed{-2} \xrightarrow{a-2} \boxed{\div 4} \rightarrow \dfrac{a-2}{4}$

$\underline{} \leftarrow \boxed{+2} \xleftarrow{28} \boxed{\times 4} \leftarrow$ The constant **7** is fed into the reverse machine.

3) $4b - 5 = 3$ $\underline{} \leftarrow \boxed{\div 4} \xleftarrow{8} \boxed{+5} \leftarrow 3$

4) $3a + 3 = 18$ $\underline{} \leftarrow \boxed{} \leftarrow \boxed{} \leftarrow 18$

5) $\dfrac{x}{4} - 10 = 6$ $\underline{} \leftarrow \boxed{} \leftarrow \boxed{} \leftarrow 6$

c. Reverse Operations

Reverse Operations can solve algebraic equations.

Example: Solve $\frac{x}{8} + 6 = 14$ with reverse operations.

The objective is to get x on its own on one side of the equation. When a term is moved to the other side its sign changes. Inverse operations apply:

```
Add ⟷ Subtract
```
```
Multiply ⟷ Divide
```

To get the x term on its own, move all constants to the opposite side.

$$\frac{x}{8} + 6 = 14 \quad \text{Turn the + 6 to − 6 by changing sides.}$$

$$\frac{x}{8} = 14 \, (- 6)$$

$$\frac{x}{8} = 8 \quad \text{Turn the ÷ 8 to × 8 by changing sides.}$$

$$x = 8 \, (\times \, 8)$$

$$x = 64$$

Exercise 19: 22b   Solve these equations:

6) $\frac{x}{4} - 7 = 1$

7) $6x + 4 = 28$

$x = $ ____

$x = $ ____

8) $18 = 3a + 3$

This equation is round the other way. Collect a on the right instead of the left, then do it in the same way.

9) $1 = 4y - 15$

$y = $ ____

10) $8x + 2 = 18$

Score

$a = $ ____

$x = $ ____

d. Balancing

The **Balancing Method** requires the unknown value to be left on one side of the equation and constants added or subtracted, as required, to make them equal to **0** on this side. The = sign acts like a weighing scale. **Whatever action is carried out on one side must be done to the other side.**

Example: | Find the value of x if $3x + 6 = 24$ |

Equations require adding and subtracting to be done before multiplying and dividing.

$$3x + 6 = 24$$

Subtract 6 from both sides.

1. Deal with add/subtract first. Subtract **6** to cancel the + **6**.

$$3x + \overset{-6}{\cancel{6}} = 24 \overset{-6}{}$$

2. Subtract **6** from **24** on the other side.

$$3x = 24 - 6$$

Divide both sides by 3.

3. $3x$ is really $3 \times x$. To get x alone we divide $3x$ by **3**.

$$\frac{\cancel{3}x}{\cancel{3}} = 18 \overset{\div 3}{}$$

4. Divide **18** by **3** to find the value of x.

$$x = \frac{18}{3}$$

5. x is now on its own.

$$x = 6$$

Exercise 19: 23a   Solve these equations:

1) $3x - 4 = 17$

   $x = \underline{\quad\quad}$

2) $3x + 9 = 36$

   $x = \underline{\quad\quad}$

3) $\frac{x}{18} + 3 = 6$

   $x = \underline{\quad\quad}$

4) $3y - 9 = 27$

   $y = \underline{\quad\quad}$

e. Variables on Both Sides

Equations with more than one variable either side can be solved in a similar way. The rule is 'get rid of the smallest letter term by moving it to the other side of the equals sign'.

Example: | Find the value of $4x - 28 = 3x + 4$ |

If an equation has two same type variables these must be combined first.

Two Variables

$$4x - 28 = 3x + 4$$

1. Cancel **3x** by subtracting.

$$4x - 28 = \cancel{3x}^{-3x} + 4$$

2. Balance by placing **-3x** from the other side.

$$4x - 3x - 28 = 4$$

3. Subtract the two letter terms **4x − 3x** to give **x**.

$$x - 28 = 4$$

4. Cancel **-28** by adding **28** to the same side.

$$x - \cancel{28}^{+28} = 4$$

5. Balance it by adding **28** to the other side.

$$x = 4 + 28$$

6. Add **4** and **28** to find **x**.

$$x = 32$$

Exercise 19: 23b   Solve these equations:

5) $2y + 3 = 13 - 3y$

6) $9 + x = 17 - 3x$

$y = $ ____

$x = $ ____

7) $2x + 2 = 5x - 4$ 8) $4x - 1 = 17 - 2x$

$x =$ _____ $x =$ _____

9) $7y - 9 = 2y + 26$ 10) $3x + 16 = 40 - 3x$

$y =$ _____ $x =$ _____   Score

f. Equations with Brackets

If equations have brackets, multiply them out and solve the equation as usual.

$$4(2x + 5) = 3(x + 10)$$
$$8x + 20 = 3x + 30$$

Exercise 19: 24a   Solve these equations:

1) $5(2x - 1) = 15$ 2) $4(2y + 5) = 3(y + 15)$

$x =$ _____ $y =$ _____

3) $2(x - 1) = 6(2x - 2)$ 4) $3(x + 2) = x + 4$

$x =$ _____ $x =$ _____

5) $7(1 + 2y) = 91$ 6) $8(x + 3) = 2(3x + 5)$

$y =$ _____ $x =$ _____

g. Equations and Substitution

Once an equation has been solved it can be checked by substitution.

Example: | Check the solution to $3x + 2 = 2x + 9$ by substitution.

1. The solution to this equation is **7**.

2. Substitute **7** into the equation.

3. The equation balances.

$$3x + 2 = 2x + 9$$
$$x = 7$$
$$(3 \times 7) + 2 = (2 \times 7) + 9$$
$$23 = 23$$

Exercise 19: 24b Solve these equations:

7) $6a - 3 = 2a + 13$

9) $2x - 5 = 5x - 11$

$a =$ _____

$x =$ _____

Substitute into the equations to check they work:

8) $6a - 3 = 2a + 13$

10) $2x - 5 = 5x - 11$

_____ = _____

_____ = _____

It balances? Yes or no? _____

It balances? Yes or no? _____

h. More Difficult Equations

More difficult equations often combine the use of brackets, fractions and negative numbers.

Example: $\boxed{\text{Calculate } 9(2 + \frac{x}{3}) = 27}$

1. Divide both sides. $\quad (2 + \frac{x}{3}) = 27 \div 9$

$\qquad\qquad\qquad (2 + \frac{x}{3}) = 3$

2. Subtract **2** and then multiply both sides by **3**.

$\qquad\qquad\qquad \frac{x}{3} = 1$

$\qquad\qquad\qquad x = 3$

Exercise 19: 25   Solve these equations:

1) $\dfrac{x}{2} - 3 = \text{-}10$

2) $12(\dfrac{z}{4} - \dfrac{1}{2}) = 0$

$x = \underline{\hspace{2cm}}$ $z = \underline{\hspace{2cm}}$

Now try these more complex equations on paper:

3) $\dfrac{m + 8}{7} = 2$

4) $2(x + 1) - 10 = \text{-}4$

$m = \underline{\hspace{1.5cm}}$ $x = \underline{\hspace{1.5cm}}$

5) $3(2x - 5) - 4(x + 7) = 13 \qquad x = \underline{\hspace{1.5cm}}$

6) $\dfrac{3x - 4}{7} = 8$

7) $\dfrac{2y - 5}{3} = \text{-}5$

$x = \underline{\hspace{1.5cm}}$ $y = \underline{\hspace{1.5cm}}$

8) $4(x + 5) - 2(x - 9) = 24 \qquad x = \underline{\hspace{1.5cm}}$

Score

9) $5(3 - 2x) = 3(4 - 3x) \qquad x = \underline{\hspace{1.5cm}}$

10) $\dfrac{1}{2}(y - 3) = y + 6 \qquad y = \underline{\hspace{1.5cm}}$

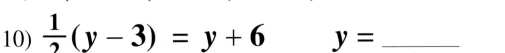

12. Algebraic Formulae
a. What is a Formula?

A **Formula** is a mathematical rule, usually written as an equation. If a number is substituted into the formula it will be changed into another number by mathematical operations. (For other Arithmetic Formulae see Maths Workbooks 1-5.)

For example, the formula for the area of a rectangle is:

Area = Length × Width (This is true for all rectangles.)

Algebraic Formulae are equations that also state a rule that can either be applied generally or just to a particular question. They use **symbols** or **letters** to denote the missing variable. Many formulae can be stated in an algebraic form.

For example, a formula for the perimeter of a square is:

P = 4L (Perimeter = 4 × Length of one side. This is true for all squares.)

b. Temperature Formulae

Degrees Fahrenheit (°F) is the old-fashioned temperature scale and **Degrees Celsius** (°C) is the modern temperature scale. Approximate conversions are shown on this table:

Standard Temperatures	Freezing Point	Room Temp	A Very Hot Day	Body Temp	Boiling Point	
Celsius	0°C	20°C	30°C	37.4°C	100°C	Celsius is calibrated using the
Fahrenheit	32°F	68°F	86°F	99.3°F	212°F	freezing and boiling point of water.

Algebraic formulae are used for difficult conversions from Fahrenheit to Celsius and vice versa.

Fahrenheit to Celsius
Substitute Fahrenheit into this formula to find Celsius.

$$C = \frac{5}{9} (F - 32)$$

Example: Convert **43°** Fahrenheit to Celsius.

$$C = \frac{5}{9}(F - 32)$$

$$C = \frac{5}{9}(43 - 32)$$

$$C = \frac{5}{9}(11)$$

$$C = (5 \div 9) \times 11$$

$$C = 0.\dot{5} \times 11$$

$$C = 6.11 \text{ (Rounds to 6.)}$$

$$43°F = 6°C$$

Exercise 19: 26a

Convert temperatures from °F to °C (round to whole degrees):

1) **67°F** = _____ °C   2) **39°F** = _____ °C

3) **59°F** = _____ °C   4) **12°F** = _____ °C

5) **80°F** = _____ °C

Celsius to Fahrenheit

Substitute Celsius into this formula to find Fahrenheit.

$$F = \frac{9}{5}C + 32$$

Example: Convert **5°** Celsius to Fahrenheit.

$$F = \frac{9}{5}C + 32$$

$$F = \frac{9}{5}5 + 32$$

$$F = (9 \div 5) \times 5 + 32$$

$$F = (1.8 \times 5) + 32$$

$$F = 9 + 32$$

$$F = 41$$

$$5°C = 41°F$$

Exercise 19: 26b

Convert temperatures from °C to °F (round to whole degrees):

6) **21°C** = _____ °F   7) **16°C** = _____ °F

8) **2°C** = _____ °F   9) **-10°C** = _____ °F

10) **27°C** = _____ °F

Score

c. Turning Words into Formulae

Statements or expressions can be converted into formulae. The Four Rules of Number $+ - \times \div$ provide the basis.

The most common statements for creating formulae from the Four Rules of Number are listed below:

Addition

> **more than;   on top of;**
> **increased by;   enlarge;**
> **added to;   plus**

Example 1:

What is **8 more than n**?

$$n + 8 \quad \text{or} \quad 8 + n$$

This can be written in two ways because addition is commutative (see p. 3).

Subtraction

> **is taken away;   from;**
> **decreased by; reduced;**
> **is removed;   less than**

Example 2:

What is **8 less than n**?

$$n - 8$$

This cannot be written as $8 - n$ because subtraction is not commutative (see p. 3).

Multiplication

> **increased by a factor of;**
> **tripled;   doubled;**
> **lots of;   quadrupled**

Example 3:

What is **8 lots of n**?

$$n8 \quad \text{or} \quad 8n$$

This can be written in two ways since multiplication is commutative (see p. 3).

Division

> **reduced by a factor of;**
> **shared out; Divided up;**
> **halved;   split between**

Example 4:

What is **8 shared out between n**?	$\longrightarrow$	$\dfrac{8}{n}$

This cannot be written as $\dfrac{n}{8}$ because division is not commutative (see p. 3).

Exercise 19: 27 Write as formulae:

1) **7** more than **n** $n + 7$

2) **b** split between **8** _____

3) Twice **y** plus **x** $2y + x$

4) **c** decreased by **7** _____

5) **3** less than **4** lots of **x** $4x - 3$

6) **5** less than **y** _____

7) **5** plus **n**, shared between **y** $5 + n \div y$

8) Triple **n** take away **6**, reduced by a factor of **4** _____

9) **x** increased by **5** then divided up by **y** _____

10) **p** halved minus **r** $(p \div 2) - r$

Score

d. Formulaic Expressions

Formulae can be used to represent and solve problems.
Look out for the Four Rules of Number $+ - \times \div$

Example: Write this sentence as an algebraic expression:
A prize of **x** pounds is shared among **4** children.
How many pounds does each child receive?

Each child receives $\dfrac{x}{4}$ pounds or $\dfrac{1}{4}x$ pounds.

Exercise 19: 28a Write as algebraic expressions:

1) A piece of cloth measures **y** metres and is cut into **5** equal lengths. Each piece measures _____ metres.

2) Tom trains for a cross country race. He runs **x** miles every day after school and twice as far on Saturday and Sunday. How many miles does he run in one week? _____ miles

3) **50** children are taken on a school trip. Each child takes £**x** for the fare and £**y** for pocket money. What is the total amount taken by the group? _____ pounds

4) Mary scored **m** marks in maths, **e** marks in English and **s** marks in science. Mary's average mark was _____.

5) Nikhil earns **x** pounds each week from his paper round. He also gets **y** pounds each month from his parents. How much does Nikhil get in one year? _____ pounds

e. Formulaic Equations

Sentences can be written as equations if their wording requires an equals sign.

is; total; is the same as; gives the same answer as; find; find the answer to

Example:

> Cooking instructions for the Christmas turkey: Allów **20mins** cooking time for each pound plus an extra **45mins**. Write a formula for the total time taken (**T**) to cook the turkey where **w** represents the weight of the turkey in lbs.

The equation can be expressed as: $T = 20w + 45$
If amounts are supplied the equation offers a solution:

$T = 20w + 45$

$T = (20 \times 15) + 45$

$T = 345mins$ or **5hrs 45mins**

How long would it take to cook a **15lb** turkey?

Exercise 19: 28b Write and solve as equations:

6) If **x** sweets cost **50p**, write down a formula for the cost (**C**) in pence of one sweet and then solve the problem below:

   a) $C =$ _____   b) What is the cost of **30** sweets? _____

7) To find **y**, square **x**, divide this by **2** and add **3**.

   a) Equation: $y =$ _____   b) If **x** is **4** find **y**. _____

8) a) There are **27** children in a class and they divide themselves into **two** equal teams (each with x children) for games. There are **9** who arrive too late to play.

i) The equation is: _____

ii) How many children in each team? _____ children

b) A boy hires a bicycle for the day whilst on holiday. He is charged **£12** for the first **5** hours, then an hourly rate of **£1.60** for each additional hour (h). i) Write down a formula (in pence) for the cost of hiring the bicycle. ii) What would it cost to hire the bicycle for **11** hours?

i) $C =$ _____ ii) **11** hours would cost £ _____ .

9) During a two day fair a school sells choc ices and tubs of ice cream. A choc ice costs **50p** and an ice cream tub costs **40p**. The income (I) is found using the equation:

$$I = 50x + 40y$$

x is the number of choc ices sold.
y is the number of ice cream tubs sold.

a) Day 1 $x = 20$ and $y = 35$, so what is I ? £ _____

b) Day 2 $I = 2000$ and $x = 16$, so what is y? _____

[handwritten in margin: $2x + 4 = 14 + x$, $3x + 4 = 14$]

Questions are more complex if the equation has to be created from two binomial expressions.

Example: Write this sentence as an algebraic equation:

Paula found that if she multiplied the number of sweets (x) she had by **5** and subtracted **2** it was **the same as** if she added **18** to the number of sweets.

If the number of sweets was x, multiplying by **5** and subtracting **2** would give the expression: $5x - 2$

Adding **18** to the number of sweets (x) gives: $x + 18$

Equating these expressions gives: $5x - 2 = x + 18$

This can now be solved: $5x - 2 = x + 18$

$x = 5$ sweets

$5x = x + 20$

$4x = 20$

Exercise 19: 28c Find and solve the equation:

10) a) Ben worked out that if he took his age (**x**), multiplied it by **2** and added **4**, it would give the same answer as adding **14** to his age.

   i) Equation: $x2 + 4$ = $14 + x$ ii) Solution: *x* = _10_

   b) Andy counted his savings. He found that if he took the amount of money he had (**y**), multiplied it by **4** and then subtracted **9**, he would get the same amount as if he counted the money he had and added **15** pounds.

   i) Equation: _____ = _____   ii) Solution: *y* = _____

f. Formulae and Diagrams

Drawing **Diagrams** can help you understand some questions.

Example 1: | Hamza will be **x** years old **8** years from now. How old was he **8** years ago?

1. Start from now.
2. **x** is **8** years from now.
3. Count back from now **8** years to find out how old Hamza was **8** years ago.

Now   **+ 8**

●————————→**x**

$x - 16$ ←———— **− 8** ●——— **Now** ——— **+ 8** ———→**x**

Hamza was *x* − 16 years eight years ago.

Example 2: John and Priya plant some tomato seeds on the same day. After **1** week both seedlings are **7cm** tall. During the next **three** weeks John's seedling grows **ycm** per week and Priya's grows **xcm** per week. Priya's plant is taller. When the seedlings are **four** weeks old how much taller is Priya's seedling than John's in cm?

1. Both seedlings are the same height after the first week so this can be ignored.
2. Priya's seedling grows taller.
3. The difference between Priya's and John's seedlings is:

$3(x - y)$ Priya's seedling is this much taller.

Priya (x)   John (y)

3 weeks is 3x

Priya's seedling is taller by $3(x - y)$

3 weeks is 3y

1st week

7cm

Exercise 19: 29a   Answer the following:

1) a) In **3** years time Charlotte's dog will be **x** years old. How old was her dog **8** years ago? _____

___

b) A batsman is bowled out after scoring **r** runs. If he had scored **10** more runs he would have **twice** as many as the batsman before him who scored **20**. Write an equation with **r** to show how many runs he scored and then solve it.

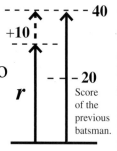

40

+10

20
Score of the previous batsman.

r

i) Equation: _____   ii) Solution: **r** = _____

___

c) If you multiply a number (**x**) by **3**, then double it and divide by **6**, the result is **5**. Find the value of **x**.

Solve with inverse operations - reverse function machine.

x = _____   ⬅ ☐ ⊢ ☐ ⊢ ☐ ⬅ 5

Example 3:

P 10+

> Paul has saved **£10** more than Naveen. Naveen has saved **£3** more than Janet. Altogether Paul, Naveen and Janet have saved **£26.20**. How much did each save individually?

It is best to represent this information diagrammatically. This will make it easier to see how the amounts given relate to each other.

We can show that Paul has **£10** more than Naveen and that Naveen has **£3** more than Janet.

Paul	**Naveen**	**Janet** ←	
£10 more			**Total**
£?	**£3 more**		**£26.20**
Unknown Amounts Saved		←	

The missing amount under Paul **£?** can be filled in. It must be **£3**. Paul therefore has **£13** more than Janet. The unknown amounts that Paul, Naveen and Janet without the differences can be represented as **3x**.

Paul	**Naveen**	**Janet** ←	
£10			**Total**
£3	**£3**		**£26.20**
x	*x*	*x* ←	

Janet's savings are worked out by finding the value of x, Naveen's savings by finding the value of $x + 3$ and Paul's savings by finding the value of $x + 13$. When added, they equal the total savings of **£26.20**. This gives the linear equation of:

$$3x + 16 = 26.20$$

$$3x + 16 = 26.20$$
$$3x = 26.20 - 16$$
$$3x = 10.20$$
$$x = 3.40$$

Janet saved **£3.40** (*x*).
Naveen saved (*x* + **£3**),
so Naveen saved **£6.40**
and Paul saved (*x* + **£13**),
so Paul saved **£16.40**.

Exercise 19: 29b   Answer the following:

2) Zak, Murrey and Philip play for the same football team.
They score a total of **50** goals during the season. Zak
scores **5** fewer than Murrey who scores **4** fewer than
Philip. How many goals does each player score?

Zak	**Murrey**	**Philip** ↰	
		4 more	**Total**
	5 more	**?**	**50**
Unknown no. of goals Scored ↰			**goals**

The linear equation will be: _____ = _____

Zak scores _____ goals, Murrey scores _____ goals
and Philip scores _____ goals.

---

3) Brighde, Nichol, Rory and Holly collect stamps. They
have **144** stamps altogether. Brighde has **21** more than
Nichol, Rory has **8** fewer than Nichol and Rory has **9**
more than Holly. How many does each person have?

The linear equation will be: _____ = _____

Brighde collects _____ stamps, Nichol collects _____
stamps, Rory collects _____ stamps and Holly collects
_____ stamps.

g. Formulae and Shapes
(i) Perimeter

Perimeter Formula can be expressed algebraically.

Example: Find the perimeter of a rectangle **(4x + 2)** centimetres long and **2x** centimetres wide.

1. Add together the lengths of all the sides.

$$(4x + 2) + 2x + (4x + 2) + 2x$$

2. Simplify as far as possible.

$$(12x + 4) = 4(3x + 1)\text{cm}$$

2x

(4x + 2)

Exercise 19: 29c Write as formulae:

4) a) Write the perimeter of this shape as an algebraic expression. (Don't forget to simplify.)

_____

b) Write the perimeter of this shape as a formula:

Perimeter
= _____

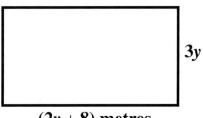

c) What is the perimeter of this shape?

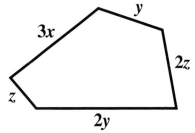

Perimeter
= _____ km

d) The perimeter of this shape can be written as:

Set out: _____

Simplify: _____ m

3y

(2y + 8) metres

(ii) Area

The **Area** of shapes can also be written algebraically:

Area of a Rectangle = Length × Width   **Area = L × W**

Example 1: | Calculate the area of a rectangle **(9n – 4)** metres long and **5n** metres wide.

$$(9n - 4)$$

Area = Length × Width

Area = (9n – 4) × 5n

Area = (45n² – 20n)m²

$5n$

It is better to write square metres in full to avoid confusion as the *n* value has also been squared.

Area of the Rectangle $= (45n^2 - 20n)$ **square metres**

Example 2: | Write a formula for the area of this octagon.

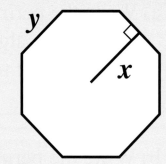

y

x

1. Notice that the octagon breaks into triangles if the diagonals are drawn in.

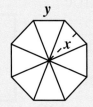

y

x

2. The area formula for each triangle is:

Area = $\frac{1}{2}$ Base × Height

3. Algebraically the formula is:

Area = $\frac{1}{2}yx$

4. Multiply by **8** for the area of the octagon:

Area = $8 \times \frac{1}{2}yx$

Area of the octagon = 4yx = 4xy

Exercise 19: 29d Write as formulae:

5) a) One side of the square
  is **n**cm. Write the area
  and perimeter as formulae:

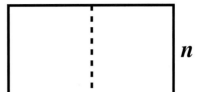

  i) Area = _____

  ii) Perimeter = _____

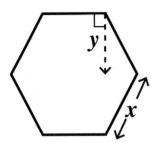

b) What is the formula for the area
  of this shape?

  Underline the correct answer.

  i) $x^2 + y^2$ ii) $x - y$ iii) **3xy**   iv) **2xy**

c) Write the area for the rectangle
  (**3x + 2**) metres in length and **2x**
  metres in width.

  Area = _____ square metres

(**3x + 2**)

d) The length of a carpet is **3 times** its width. Its width
  is **2y** metres. The formula for the area is:

  i) Area = _____

  ii) The area = _____ square metres

  iii) Perimeter = _____

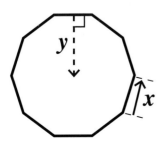

e) i) What is the formula for the area
    of this decagon?

    Area = _____

  ii) What is the area if x = **2cm** and
    y = **3cm**? Area = _____ cm^2

(iii) Volume

The **Volume** of a Cuboid = Length × Width × Height

Example: Find the volume of a cuboid **4a** metres long, **3a** metres wide and **a** metres high.

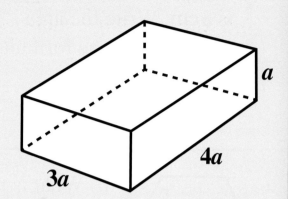

Volume = $\mathbf{L \times W \times H}$

Volume = $\mathbf{4a \times 3a \times a = 12a^3 cm^3}$

It is better to write cubic metres in full to avoid confusion as the **a** value has also been cubed.

Volume of the cuboid = $\mathbf{12a^3}$ **cubic metres**

Exercise 19: 29e Write as formulae:

6) a)

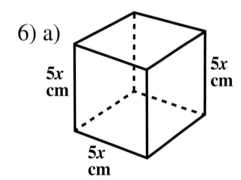

Volume of the cube = _____ cubic centimetres

b)

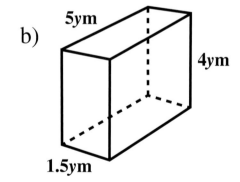

Volume of the cuboid = _____ cubic metres

c) A matchbox has length **75z** millimetres, width **45z** millimetres and height **20z** millimetres.

Volume of the matchbox = _____ cubic millimetres

h. Trial and Substitution with Formulae
(i) Creating the Formula

Questions may require creation of formulae and **Trialling and Substituting** quantities for the unknown variables.

Example: | Two brothers eat Shredded Bisks for breakfast. A Shredded Bisk box contains **20** bisks. Peter eats x bisks and John eats y bisks each day. Peter eats more than John. After **3** days there are **5** bisks left in the box. Which answer is correct?
a) $x = 2$ and $y = 3$ b) $x = 3$ and $y = 1$
c) $x = 3$ and $y = 2$

1) Create the formula:

Peter eats x bisks and John eats y bisks every day for three days. Peter eats more than John. In all they eat **15** bisks, which can be shown as:

$$3(x + y) = 15$$

Divide both sides by 3:

$$x + y = 5$$

Remember: whatever we do to one side of the equation to simplify it, we must also do to the other.

a) $x = 2$ and $y = 3$
These values cannot work since John would be eating more than Peter.

b) $x = 3$ and $y = 1$
$x + y$
$3 + 1 = 4$
The amount is too low.

c) $x = 3$ and $y = 2$
$x + y$
$3 + 2 = 5$
This fits the formula.

Exercise 19: 29f   Answer the following:

7) **Three** cars race on a racetrack. **Forty** litres of fuel are available for the race. When the race is over **five** litres of fuel are left. The red car (r) uses more fuel than the other two cars put together for each circuit. The green car (g) does not use as much fuel as the blue car (b) for each circuit. The cars complete **5** circuits of the racetrack.

a) Write the formula: _____

b) Which values are correct? _____

   i) $g = 4$; $b = 3$; $r = 2$ ii) $r = 3$; $b = 2$; $g = 2$
   iii) $r = 4$; $b = 2$; $g = 1$ iv) $b = 4$; $g = 2$; $r = 7$

(ii) Creating the Values

Questions sometimes give a formula. Values have to be created, which are then substituted into the formula to find another formula that also gives the same result.

Example 1:

x is $\dfrac{3}{4}$ of y	Which answer has the same value? a) $9x = 16y$ b) $12x = 16y$ c) $20x = 15y$ d) $5x = 4y$

This could be written as $x = \dfrac{3}{4}y$ values are then created:

If we give x a value of **3**, as this is three-quarters of y, the value of y must be **4** ($x = 3$ and $y = 4$).

These values can now be tested in the alternatives:

a) $9x = 16y \rightarrow 9 \times 3 = 16 \times 4 \rightarrow 27 = 64$ (Does not work.)

b) $12x = 16y \rightarrow 12 \times 3 = 16 \times 4 \rightarrow 36 = 64$ (Does not work.)

d) $5x = 4y \rightarrow 5 \times 3 = 4 \times 4 \rightarrow 15 = 16$ (Does not work.)

However:

c) $20x = 15y \rightarrow 20 \times 3 = 15 \times 4 \rightarrow 60 = 60$ (This works.)

The values satisfy this equation (make both sides equal).

So, $x = \dfrac{3}{4}y$ is the same as $20x = 15y$.

We should check this with more values where x is $\dfrac{3}{4}$ of y, such as $x = 6$ and $y = 8$:

$\qquad 20x = 15y \rightarrow 20 \times 6 = 15 \times 8 \rightarrow 120 = 120$ (This works.)

Example 2:

A year 5 class make some formula cards. Which two cards have the same value?

$3(2x - 4)$	$3x + 5$	$2(x - 4)$	$2(3x - 6)$

Using $x = 1$:

$3(2x - 4) = 3(2 \times 1 - 4) = \text{-}6 \qquad 3x + 5 = 3 \times 1 + 5 = 8$

$2(x - 4) = 2(1 - 4) = \text{-}6 \qquad\qquad 2(3x - 6) = 2(3 \times 1 - 6) = \text{-}6$

However, the two cards should give the same value for any substitution of x. So we can try values of $x = 2, ...$ and we find that $3(2x - 4)$ and $2(3x - 6)$ always give the same value.

Exercise 19: 29g Answer the following:

8) a) x is $\frac{1}{2}$ of y

Which of the following is correct?

i) $\frac{y}{x} = 2x$ ii) $y = 2x$ iii) $x = 2y$

iv) $x = \frac{y}{3}$ v) $\frac{x}{y} = \frac{1}{4}$

---

b) A teacher has **6** bags of sweets and **3** loose sweets. Each bag has s sweets in it. i) Which expression shows how many sweets there are altogether? _____

$6s - 4$ $6s + 3$ ii) If there are **105** sweets altogether, what is the value of s? _____

$s + 6$ $3 + s$

---

9) a) Some cards have these expressions written on them:

$2x + 6$ $x + 5$ $3x + 5$ $2x + 3$

i) Using the substitution $x = 1$, which cards give the same value as $2(x + 3)$? _____
ii) Use the substitution $x = 2$ to find which card always gives the same value as $2(x + 3)$.
The correct card is _____ .

---

b) $x + 2y = 4z$

i) Substitute $x = 2$ and $z = 3$ into the above equation to work out the value of y. _____
ii) Substitute the above three values into the following equations. Underline the equation that does not equate.

$x + 2y - 4z = 0$ $3x + 6y = 12z$

$x = 4z - 2y$ $0 = x + 2y - 4z$

$2y = 4z + x$

(iii) Creating the Formula and the Values

Some questions require the creation of both the formula and the values for trial and substitution:

Example: | Choc bars (*c*) cost the same as sugar dips (*s*). Sugar dips cost twice as much as toffee chews (*t*). Four of the following cost the same. Which does not cost the same as the rest?
a) **2** choc bars, **2** sugar dips, **2** toffee chews
b) **3** sugar dips, **2** toffee chews, **1** choc bar
c) **3** sugar dips, **2** choc bars
d) **1** choc bar, **6** toffee chews, **1** sugar dip
e) **2** choc bars, **4** toffee chews, **2** sugar dips

A formula can be created using a ratio:

1 choc bar : 1 sugar dip : 2 toffee chews

$$c \; : \; s \; : \; 2t$$

Values can be substituted in to make the ratio work.

2p choc bar : 2p sugar dip : 1p toffee chews

These values can now be substituted into each possibility. Each correct combination should make an equation.

a) **2** choc bars, **2** sugar dips, **2** toffee chews

$\quad$ 2c $\qquad\qquad$ 2s $\qquad\qquad$ 2t
$(2 \times 2p) + (2 \times 2p) + (2 \times 1p) =$
$4p + 4p + 2p = 10p$ $\quad$ (This is correct.)

b) **3** sugar dips, **2** toffee chews, **1** choc bar

$\quad$ 3s $\qquad\qquad$ 2t $\qquad\qquad$ 1c
$(3 \times 2p) + (2 \times 1p) + (1 \times 2p) =$
$6p + 2p + 2p = 10p$ $\quad$ (This is correct.)

c) **3** sugar dips, **2** choc bars

$\quad$ 3s $\qquad\qquad$ 2c
$(3 \times 2p) + (2 \times 2p) =$
$6p + 2p + 2p = 10p$ $\quad$ (This is correct.)

d) **1** choc bar, **6** toffee chews, **1** sugar dip

     1c   **6t**   **1s**

(1 × 2p) + (6 × 1p) + (1 × 2p) =

2p + 6p + 2p = 10p   (This is correct.)

e) **2** choc bars, **4** toffee chews, **2** sugar dips

     2c   **4t**   **2s**

(2 × 2p) + (4 × 1p) + (2 × 2p) =

4p + 4p + 4p = 12p   (This is different and

                                   therefore incorrect.)

Answer: e) 4p + 4p + 4p = 12p

2 choc bars, **4** toffee chews, **2** sugar dips

Exercise 19: 29h Answer the following: **Score**

10) A stack of **4** identical apple boxes (***a***) weighs the same as a stack of **6** identical orange boxes (***o***). Which of the following statements is incorrect?

   a) **8** apple boxes weigh the same as **12** orange boxes.

   b) **3** orange boxes weigh the same as **2** apple boxes.

   c) **15** orange boxes weigh the same as **10** apple boxes.

   d) **12** apple boxes weigh the same as **18** orange boxes.

   e) **10** orange boxes weigh the same as **8** apple boxes.

Statement _____ is incorrect.

13. Graphs and Lines
a. Points on a Line

Lines are drawn from plotting *x* and *y* coordinates (see Maths Workbook 5). A minimum of **two** coordinates is required but **three** are usually plotted to ensure accuracy.

Example:

Plot coordinates and draw the line of (**1, 2**); (**0, 0**); (**-1, -2**)

Table of Values

x	1	0	-1
y	2	0	-2

Exercise 19: 30a

Answer the following:

1) Plot the coordinates and draw **Line A** from the table of values:

x	-2	0	3
y	3	1	-2

2) Fill in the table of values from the plotted coordinates of **Line B**:

x			
y			

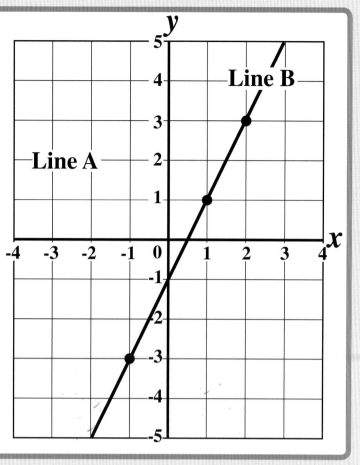

b. Horizontal, Vertical and Diagonal Lines

A **Horizontal Line** parallel to the **x-axis** is known as $y = a$.

A **Vertical Line** parallel to the **y-axis** is known as $x = a$.

Example: Draw lines $y = 3$ and $x = 6$

The **y-coordinate** for all three points is **3**.

$y = 3$

x	-3	2	4
y	3	3	3

The **x-axis** is the line: $y = 0$

The **x-coordinate** for all three points is **6**.

$x = 6$

x	6	6	6
y	4	1	-2

The **y-axis** is the line: $x = 0$

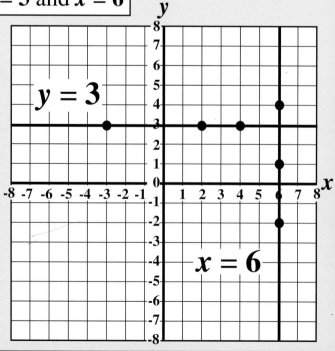

A **45° Diagonal Line** bottom left to top right is denoted $y = x$.
A **45° Diagonal Line** top left to bottom right is denoted $y = \text{-}x$.

Example: | Draw lines $y = x$ and $y = \text{-}x$ |

Both $y = x$ and $y = \text{-}x$ go through the origin $(0, 0)$.

y and x coordinates are **equal** at every point.

$y = x$

x	-6	2	6
y	-6	2	6

y and x coordinates are **equally opposite** at every point.

$y = \text{-}x$

x	-3	1	4
y	3	-1	-4

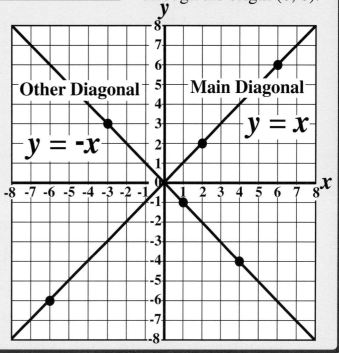

Exercise 19: 30b Identify the following lines:

3)

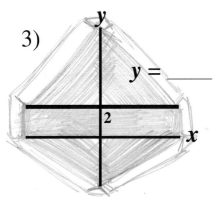

$y = \underline{\hspace{1cm}}$

4)

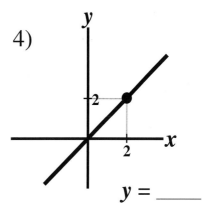

$y = \underline{\hspace{1cm}}$

5)

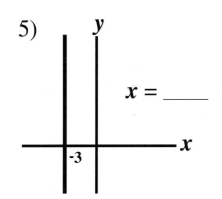

$x = \underline{\hspace{1cm}}$

6)

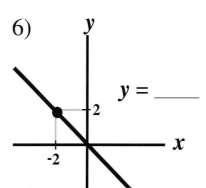

$y = \underline{\hspace{1cm}}$

14. Representing Linear Equations

A linear equation can be expressed in four different ways:

The four ways that $y = 2x + 1$ can be expressed are shown below:

1. **Function Machines** - Once the equation is fed into the machine it passes through two stages:

$$x \rightarrow \boxed{\times 2} \rightarrow 2x \rightarrow \boxed{+1} \rightarrow 2x + 1$$

$$\text{1. } y = 2x \longrightarrow \text{2. } y = 2x + 1$$

2. **Table of Values** - **x-values** can be given but, if not, you must choose them. Choose sensible values like:

$(\textbf{-2}, \textbf{-1}, \textbf{0}, \textbf{1} \text{ and } \textbf{2})$ x is between **-2** and **2**. This can be written:

$\textbf{-2} \leqslant \textbf{x} \leqslant \textbf{2}$ x is more than or equal to **-2**; x is less than or equal to **2**.

Each **x-value** is substituted into the number machine or equation to create a table of values:

x	-2	-1	0	1	2
y	-3	-1	1	3	5

Substituting into the equation is the standard method.

$$y = 2x + 1$$
$$y = (2 \times \text{-2}) + 1$$
$$y = \text{-4} + 1$$
$$y = \text{-3}$$

3. **Mappings** - If an equation is fed into a mapping it passes through two stages, just as it does in a function machine:

$$\text{1. } y = 2x \longrightarrow \text{2. } y = 2x + 1$$

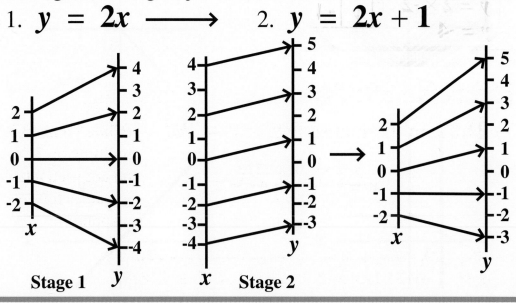

Stage 1   Stage 2

The first two diagrams break the rule down into two parts.
The third mapping does the rule in one step.

4. **Graphs** - Linear equations can be shown on a line graph.

To draw a line from an equation
a table of values has to be created:

Choose **3** values for x and substitute into the equation:

$$y = 2x + 1$$
$$y = (2 \times \text{-}2) + 1$$
$$y = \text{-}3$$

x	-2	0	2
y	-3	1	5

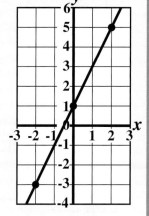

The x and y coordinates are plotted
from the table of values.

All linear equations when plotted will form a **straight line**.

15. Mappings

A **Mapping** represents a
mathematical rule or equation.

Example: Make up a table of
values and draw a
mapping for $y = 2x$

If $x = \text{-}2$
$y = 2x$
$y = 2 \times \text{-}2$
$y = \text{-}4$

x	-2	-1	0	1	2
y	-4	-2	0	2	4

$$y = 2x$$

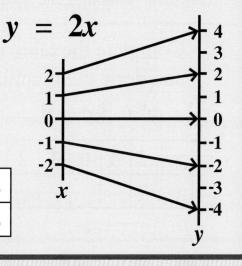

Exercise 19: 30c Answer the following:

7) Draw in the mapping for: $y = 3x$

(Clue: Think of it as multiply by **3**. You do not need a table of values for this mapping.)

65

8) Complete the table of values and draw the mapping for: $y = x - 3$

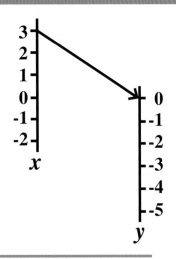

Substitute into the equation to find values:

x	-2	-1	0	1	2	3
y	-5					

$y = x - 3$
$y = -2 - 3$
$y = -5$

$y = x - 3$
$y = -1 - 3$
$y = -4$

$y = x - 3$
$y = 0 - 3$
$y = -3$

---

9) Complete the table and draw the mapping for: $y = x^2$

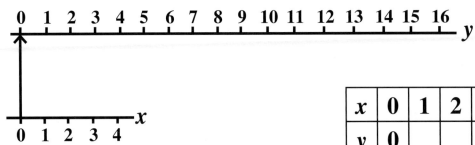

x	0	1	2	3	4
y	0				

This involves finding the square.

---

10) Complete the table of values and draw the mapping for:

Don't forget to substitute to find the values for the table.

$$y = 3x - 1$$

x	-2	-1	0	1	2
y	-7				

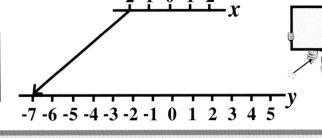

Score

16. Graphs and Linear Equations

Every linear equation in two variables can be written in the form:

$$y = mx + c$$

m is the **Gradient** (steepness) of the line or the *x*-**coefficient** on the *x*-**axis**. If *m* has a minus value the gradient is **negative**.

c is the **Gradient Intercept** on the *y*-**axis**.

Example: Show that $y = 2x + 1$ demonstrates the pattern for all linear equations:

$$y = 2x + 1$$

The gradient of the line is **2**.

The gradient intercept on the **y-axis** is **1**.

There are three ways to draw linear graphs:
a. The **Plot the Points** method (pp. 67-68).
b. The **Cover and Draw** method (pp. 69-70).
c. The **Gradient Intercept** method (pp. 70-73).

a. Plot the Points Method

You only need two points to draw a straight line, but it is always best to use three just in case a mistake is made.

Example: Draw lines $y = \dfrac{x}{3} - 2$ and $y = x + 4$

1. Create a table of values for each linear equation by choosing three **x-values** and substituting into each equation.
2. Plot each point on the **x** and **y** axes and join up the dots.

$y = \dfrac{x}{3} - 2$

x	-3	0	3
y	-3	-2	-1

$y = \dfrac{x}{3} - 2$

$y = \dfrac{-3}{3} - 2$

$y = -1 - 2$

$y = -3$

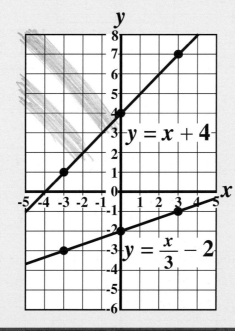

$y = x + 4$

x	-3	0	3
y	1	4	7

$y = x + 4$

$y = -3 + 4$

$y = 1$

Exercise 19: 31a   Answer the following:

1) a) Complete the table of values and draw the line for the equation:

$$y = 3x - 2$$

x	0	1	2
y	-2		

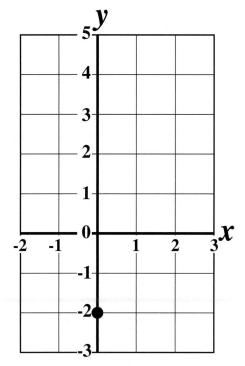

b) Does the line have a positive or negative gradient? _____

---

2) a) Using the mapping below choose three x and y values, then fill in the table of values and draw the line:

$$y = \frac{x}{2} - 1$$

$$y = \frac{x}{2} - 1$$

$$y = \frac{-4}{2} - 1$$

$$y = -2 - 1$$

$$y = -3$$

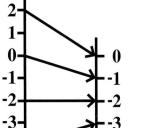

x			
y			

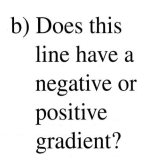

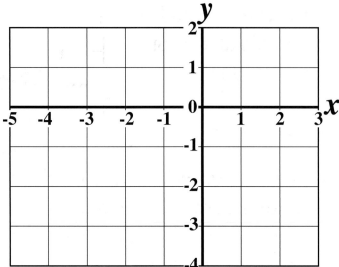

b) Does this line have a negative or positive gradient?

_____

b. Cover and Draw Method

If an equation is written in this form it can be solved simply by the Cover Up rule:

$$ax + by = c$$

Example: Draw the graph of $2x + 3y = 12$ using the cover and draw method.

To find the x coordinate of the point where the line crosses the x-axis: Ignore the $3y$ (set $y = 0$).

$$2x + \boxed{3y} = 12$$
$$2x = 12$$
$$x = 6$$

The line crosses the x-axis at ($x = 6$; $y = 0$).

To find the y coordinate of the point where the line crosses the y-axis: Ignore the $2x$ (set $x = 0$).

$$\boxed{2x} + 3y = 12$$
$$3y = 12$$
$$y = 4$$

The line crosses the y-axis at ($x = 0$; $y = 4$).

This method only gives two coordinates.

The line crosses the x-axis at **6** and the y-axis at **4**. Plot these points and join them up to form the line.

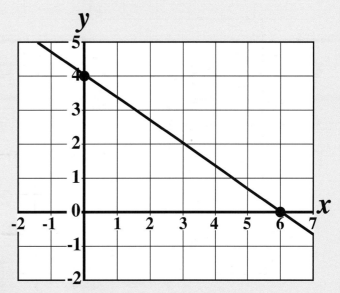

Why it works: When the line crosses the y-axis the x-value is zero and when the line crosses the x-axis the y-value is zero. This means that both the y-value and x-value can be calculated by simply ignoring other values.

Exercise 19: 31b Answer the following:

3) a) Plot and draw
the following line:

$$3x - 5y = 15$$

b) Is the gradient
negative or positive?

_____

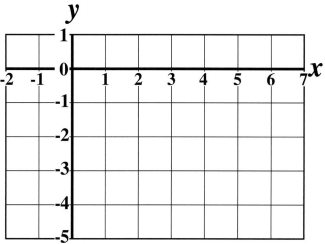

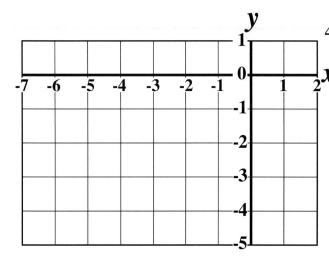

4) a) Plot and draw
the following line:

$$2x + 5y = \text{-}10$$

b) Is the gradient
negative or positive?

_____

c. Gradient Intercept Method

A line can be drawn from a linear equation by using two
pieces of information contained in the equation.

Example: | Draw the graph of $y = 2x + 1$ using
the gradient intercept method.

$$y = 2x + 1$$

1. **Gradient**
of the line is **2**
(Steepness of the line.)

2. **Gradient**
Intercept is **1**
(The point where the
line cuts the **y-axis**.)

We know that the line will cross the **y-axis** at **+1** and this is the **Gradient** (or *y*) **Intercept Point**.

The **Gradient** is **2** and this gives the steepness of the line. The whole number **2** can be written as a fraction: $\frac{2}{1}$

Algebraically the gradient formula expresses it as:

$$\textbf{Gradient} = \frac{\textbf{\textit{y}-step}}{\textbf{\textit{x}-step}} = \frac{\textbf{2}}{\textbf{1}} = \textbf{2}$$

This means for every **x-step** of **1** there is a **y-step** of **2**.

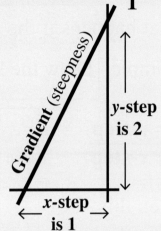

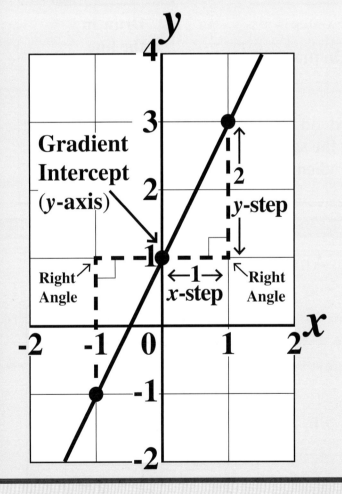

Drawing the Line

1. **x-step** - Draw a horizontal line of **1-step** out from either side of the gradient intercept point.
2. Draw a right angle.
3. **y-step** - Draw a vertical line of **2-steps** up and down from the right angle.
4. Extend the line in either direction.

Gradient defines the relationship between *x* and *y*. (How many *y* per *x*?) Gradient of a line can be used for various calculations, e.g. Ratio as a Gradient (see Maths Workbook 3), Conversion and Travel Graphs (see Maths Workbook 5).

The **x-coefficient** has no sign.

Lines that slope like this have **positive gradients**.

Lines that slope like this have **negative gradients**.

The **x-coefficient** has a minus sign.

What happens if the gradient is a **fraction** and **negative**?

Example: | Draw the line of the gradient of: $-\dfrac{1}{3}$

$\dfrac{1 = y\text{-step}}{3 = x\text{-step}}$

When this line is drawn it gives a **shallow negative gradient**:

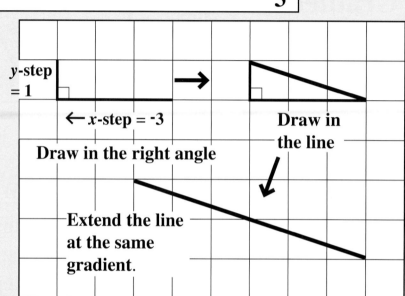

y-step = 1

← x-step = -3

Draw in the right angle

Draw in the line

Extend the line at the same gradient.

Exercise 19: 31c   Answer the following:

5) a) Plot and draw the following line:

$$y = -2x$$

1. The gradient intercept point in this equation is **0**.

2. The gradient is **-2**.

$$\dfrac{y\text{-step}}{x\text{-step}} = \dfrac{2}{1}$$ The minus sign indicates gradient.

b) Does this line have a negative or positive gradient? _____

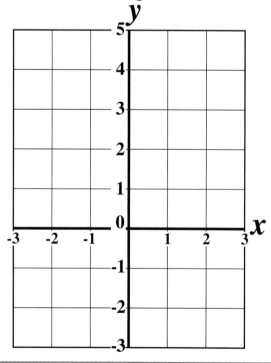

6) a) Plot and draw the following line:

$$y = \frac{x}{2} + 2$$

1. The gradient intercept point is **2**.

2. The gradient term is

$$\frac{x}{2} = \frac{1x}{2}$$

Now calculate the gradient. $\frac{\textbf{y-step}}{\textbf{x-step}} = \frac{1}{2}$

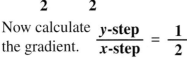

b) Is the gradient positive or negative? _____

17. Quadratic (Bucket) Graphs

Bucket Shaped or **Curved Graphs** have equations with x^2 in them. They are often in the form:

$$y = x^2 + a$$

a is the **point of intercept** on the **y-axis**.

Substitute in values for *x* to calculate *y*.

Example: Draw the bucket graph for: $y = x^2 - 2$

1. Make a table of values using **-3** to **3**. (Choose a set of values - include negative and positive values in the table):

Substitute *x* values into the equation to find *y* values:

$y = x^2 - 2$
$y = (\text{-}3)^2 - 2$
$y = (\text{-}3 \times \text{-}3) - 2$
$y = 9 - 2$
$y = 7$

2. Plot points and draw graph.

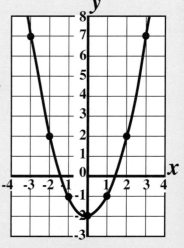

x	-3	-2	-1	0	1	2	3
y	7	2	-1	-2	-1	2	7

Exercise 19: 31d Answer the following:

7) Complete the table of values and draw the line for:

$$y = x^2 + 1$$

x	-3	-2	-1	0	1	2	3
y	10						

Substitute x values into the equation to find the y values.

$y = x^2 + 1$
$y = (-3)^2 + 1$
$y = (-3 \times -3) + 1$
$y = 9 + 1$
$y = 10$

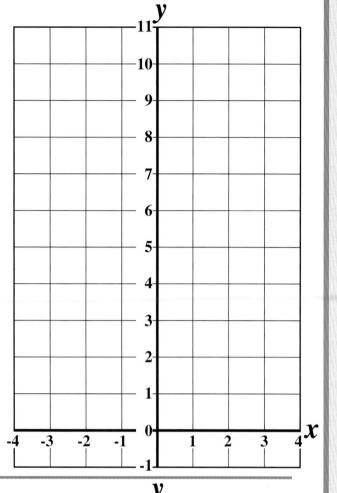

8) Complete the table of values and draw the line for:

$$y = x^2$$

x	-3						
y	9						

Substitute x values into the equation to find the y values.

$y = (-3)^2$
$y = (-3 \times -3)$
$y = 9$

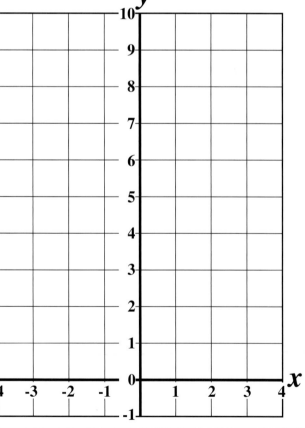

A negative sign before the x^2 sends the curve the other way.

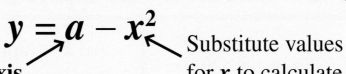

a is the point of intercept on the y-axis. $y = a - x^2$ Substitute values for x to calculate y.

Example: | Draw the bucket graph: $y = 4 - x^2$

1. Make a table of values using **-3** to **3**.

$y = 4 - x^2$
$y = 4 - (\text{-}3^2)$
$y = 4 - (\text{-}3 \times \text{-}3)$
$y = 4 - 9$
$y = \text{-}5$

Substitute x values into the equation to find y values:

x	-3	-2	-1	0	1	2	3
y	-5	0	3	4	3	0	-5

2. Plot points and draw the graph.

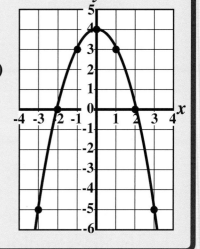

Exercise 19: 31e

Answer the following:

9) Complete the table of values and draw the line: $y = 5 - x^2$

x	-3	-2	-1	0	1	2	3
y	-4						

Substitute x values into the equation to find the y values:

$y = 5 - x^2$
$y = 5 - (\text{-}3^2)$
$y = 5 - (\text{-}3 \times \text{-}3)$
$y = 5 - 9$
$y = \text{-}4$

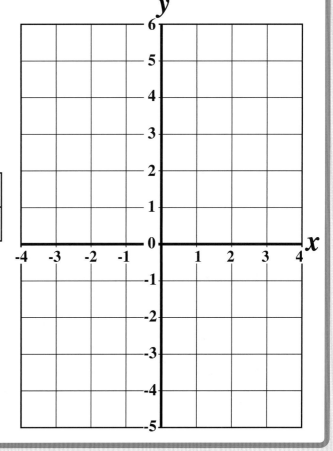

18. Cubic Graphs

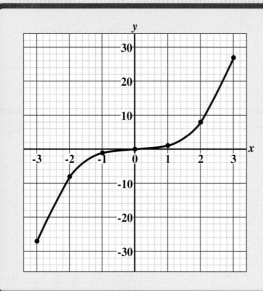

All x^3 graphs have the same basic curve.

Example: Create a table of values and draw the cubic graph: $y = x^3$

x	-3	-2	-1	0	1	2	3
y	-27	-8	-1	0	1	8	27

Exercise 19: 31f   Answer the following:

10) Complete the table of values and draw the line:

$$y = x^3 + 3$$

x	-3	-2	-1	0	1	2	3
y	-24	-5					

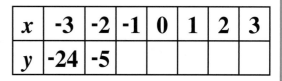

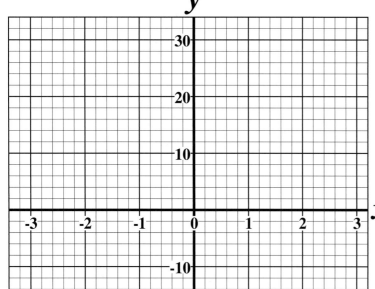

Substitute x values into the equation to find the y values

$$y = x^3 + 3$$

$$y = (\text{-}3)^3 + 3$$

Note - minus 3 × minus 3 = plus 9, but × minus 3 again = minus 27. So, $(\text{-}3)^3 = -27$.

$$y = \text{-}27 + 3$$

$$y = \text{-}24$$

$$y = x^3 + 3$$

$$y = (\text{-}2)^3 + 3$$

$$y = \text{-}8 + 3$$

$$y = \text{-}5$$

Score

19. Simultaneous Equations

Equations that have more than one variable can have an infinite number of solutions.

Example: Show the equations $2x + y = 5$ and $3x - 2y = 4$ both have more than one solution.

$2x + y = 5$

Solution 1:
$x = 2; y = 1$ $\qquad 4 + 1 = 5$

Solution 2:
$x = -1; y = 7$ $\qquad -2 + 7 = 5$

$3x - 2y = 4$

Solution 1:
$x = 2; y = 1$ $\qquad 6 - 2 = 4$

Solution 2:
$x = 6; y = 7$ $\qquad 18 - 14 = 4$

However, only one solution will fit both equations at the same time (**simultaneously**).

a. The Graphical Method

Simultaneous Equations can be solved by using the **Graphical Method** (drawing both lines on a graph). The solution to both equations is found where the two lines meet. This is called the **point of intersection**.

Example: Solve the simultaneous equations: $2x + 3y = 12$ and $y = x - 1$ using the graphical method.

$2x + 3y = 12$

Use the cover and draw method to draw the line:

Ignore the $3y$ | Ignore the $2x$

$2x + 3y = 12$ | $2x + 3y = 12$
$2x = 12$ | $3y = 12$
$x = 6$ | $y = 4$

$y = x - 1$

Create a table of values:

$y = x - 1$ | $y = x - 1$
$y = 0 - 1$ | $y = 4 - 1$
$y = -1$ | $y = 3$

$y = x - 1$
$y = 2 - 1$
$y = 1$

x	0	2	4
y	-1	1	3

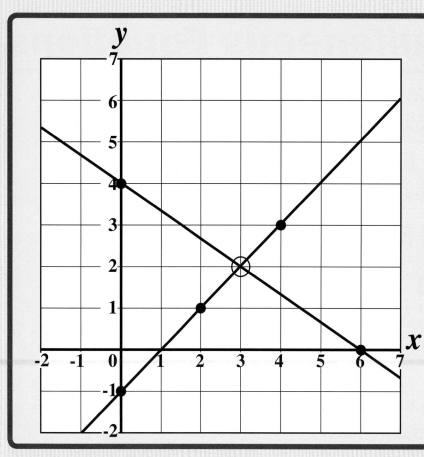

Once the lines have been plotted, the point where they meet gives the solution to the equations.

The solution to the equations is:

$$x = 3$$
$$y = 2$$

Exercise 19: 32a   Answer the following:

1) Find the solution of the simultaneous equations:

$$y = 2x - 2 \qquad y - x = 1 \longrightarrow y = x + 1$$

Change this equation to the standard format.

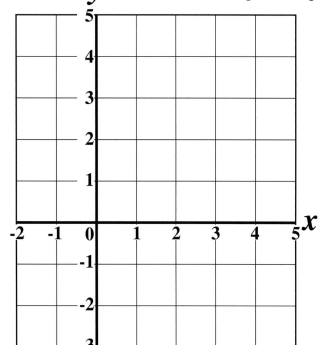

$y = 2x - 2$

x	0	1	2
y			

$y = x + 1$

x	0	1	2
y			

The solution is:

$$x = \underline{\hspace{2cm}}$$
$$y = \underline{\hspace{2cm}}$$

2) Find the solution of the simultaneous equations:

$$2x + 3y = 6$$

$$x + y = 1$$

Use the cover and draw method for both equations.

The solution is:

$x =$ _____

$y =$ _____

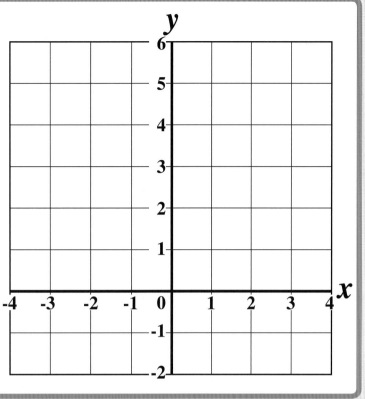

b. The Algebraic Method
(i) Solving Simultaneous Equations

To solve simultaneous equations algebraically there is a need to work through six stages:

1. Balancing   **2. Eliminating**   **3. Solving**
4. Substitution   **5. Solving again**   **6. Checking**

Example: | Solve the simultaneous equations:
$$3x + 2y = 7 \qquad 5x - 3y = 18$$

1. Balancing:
Multiply both equations by a number so that the coefficient of x in both equations matches each other.

$$3x + 2y = 7$$
$$5x - 3y = 18$$

$$3x + 2y = 7 \qquad\qquad 5x - 3y = 18$$
Multiply by **5**   Multiply by **3**

This gives two new equations with matching x values:

$$15x + 10y = 35 \qquad\qquad 15x - 9y = 54$$

2. Eliminating:

Both equations now have the same number of xs. Subtract the smaller equation from the larger equation to eliminate the x terms.

Note: $10y - {}^{-}9y$ becomes $10y + 9y$
This leaves a simple y equation.

$$15x + 10y = 35$$
$$15x - 9y = 54$$

$$15x + 10y = 35$$
$$\underline{15x - 9y = 54\ -}$$
$$19y = {}^{-}19$$

3. Solving:

Find y by solving the equation:

The y value has been found: $\boxed{y = {}^{-}1}$

$$19y = {}^{-}19$$
$$y = {}^{-}1$$

4. Substitution:

Substitute the value of y into one of the original equations.

Note: $2y = 2 \times {}^{-}1 = {}^{-}2$ (since $y = {}^{-}1$)

$$3x + 2y = 7$$
Substitute in $y = {}^{-}1$
$$3x - 2 = 7$$

5. Solve Again:

There is now a linear equation in x that can be solved in the usual way. We now have values for x and y.

$\boxed{x = 3}$ $\boxed{y = {}^{-}1}$

$$3x - 2 = 7$$
$$3x - \cancel{2} = 7 + 2$$
$$3x = 9$$
$$x = 3$$

6. Checking:

Put values $x = 3$ and $y = {}^{-}1$ into the original equations to check they work.

$$
\begin{array}{ll}
3x + 2y = 7 & 5x - 3y = 18 \\
9 + {}^{-}2 = 7 & 15 - {}^{-}3 = 18 \\
9 - 2 = 7 & 15 + 3 = 18 \\
7 = 7 & 18 = 18
\end{array}
$$

Original Equations
$$3x + 2y = 7$$
$$5x - 3y = 18$$

Both the equations balance, meaning $x = 3$ and $y = {}^{-}1$ are correct values.

Exercise 19: 32b Solve the simultaneous equations:

3) $3x - 4y = 7$ and $x + 2y = 9$

i) Balance the equations: _____ _____

ii) Eliminate the x values: _____

_____ –
_____

Subtract the equations: _____
_____

iii) Solve the y equation: _____

iv) Substitute the y value into
one of the original equations: _____

v) Solve the equation to find
the x value: _____

vi) Check the x and y values in
both equations: $x =$ _____ $y =$ _____

4) $3x - 5y = 0$ and $2x + 7y = 31$ $x =$ _____ $y =$ _____

5) $4a + 5b = 4$ and $6a + 4b = 20$ $a =$ _____ $b =$ _____

6) $3x - y = 8$ and $2x + 2y = 8$ $x =$ _____ $y =$ _____

(ii) Solving Simultaneous Problems

Simultaneous Problems involve creating the simultaneous equation before a solution can be found.

Example: Gavin and Daniel prepare for a sleepover. Gavin buys **2** packets of crisps (*c*) and **7** packets of sweets (*s*) costing **£5.70**. His friend Daniel buys **3** packets of crisps (*c*) and **4** packets of sweets (*s*) costing **£4.00**. Create the pair of simultaneous equations and find the cost of each packet.

1. Convert both statements into simultaneous equations:

     $2c + 7s = 570$ $3c + 4s = 400$

2. Perform the six stages to find cost solutions to c and s.

   Cost of crisps (*c*) = 40p   **Cost of sweets (*s*) = 70p**

Exercise 19: 32c Solve the following: Score [   ]

7-8) Rory and his sister Anna go to the seaside for the weekend. During their stay, Rory buys **3** colas (*c*) and **5** ice creams (*i*) costing **£6.30**. Anna buys **4** colas (*c*) and **3** ice creams (*i*) costing **£5.10**.

7) The equations are: _____ _____

8) A cola (*c*) costs ____p. An ice cream (*i*) costs ____p.

9-10) It costs **£138** for **6** teachers (*t*) and **48** pupils (*p*) to go on a trip to the theatre. Another group of **5** teachers (*t*) and **22** pupils (*p*) paid **£70** for the same theatre trip.

9) The equations are: _____ _____

10) A teacher (*t*) paid £ _____ . A pupil (*p*) paid £ _____ .

20. From Graphs to Equations

If a graph is given and the equation of the line or the gradient has to be identified, the best way to tackle it is by the **gradient intercept method**.

Example: | What is the equation of this graph? |

1. The gradient intercept point is **2**.

2. The gradient (**x-coefficient**):

$$= \frac{y\text{-step}}{x\text{-step}} = \frac{3}{1} = 3$$

3. The equation can now be constructed: $y = 3x + 2$

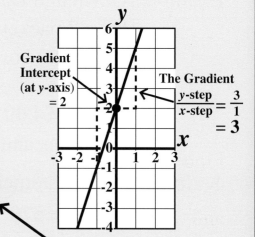

3 is the gradient (steepness) of the line or the **x-coefficient** on the **x-axis**. If it has a minus value the gradient is negative.

2 is the gradient intercept on the **y-axis**.

Exercise 19: 33 Find the gradient of these lines:

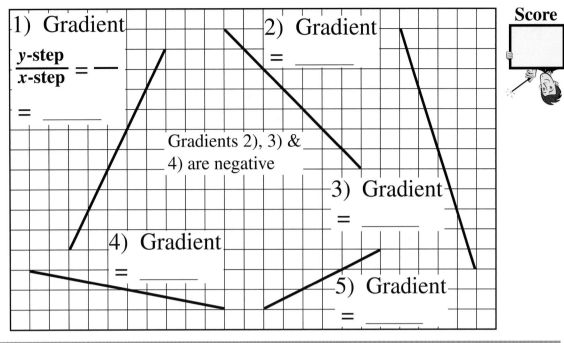

1) Gradient

$\dfrac{y\text{-step}}{x\text{-step}} = \dfrac{}{}$

= _____

2) Gradient

= _____

Gradients 2), 3) &
4) are negative

3) Gradient

= _____

4) Gradient

= _____

5) Gradient

= _____

Find the equations of
the following lines:

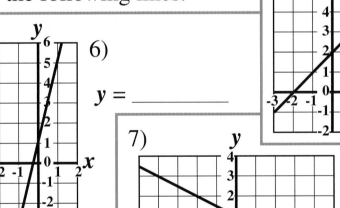

6)

y = _____

7)

y = _____

8)

y = _____

9)

y = _____

Find with
the cover
and draw
method:

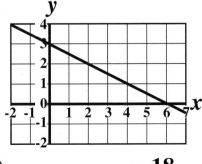

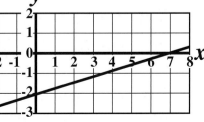

10) a) _____ = **18**   b) _____ = **14**

© 2006 Stephen Curran

21. Algebra Problems

Exercise 19: 34 Answer the following:

1) A teacher asked a class to add up algebraic expressions:

$$2x + 3$$
$$x - 2$$
$$x + 6$$
$$x$$

3 pupils gave these answers:

Rikesh: $3x + 4$

Seneesh: $5x + 7$

Tim: $5x - 7$

a) Which pupil is correct?

_____

b) If x is **3** what is the correct expression worth?

_____

---

2) A class bakes cakes. Andy bakes c cakes. Betty bakes **4** more cakes than Andy. Colin bakes **3** times as many cakes as Andy. Denise bakes **5** less cakes than Colin.

Name	Cakes
Andy	c
Betty	a) _____
Colin	b) _____
Denise	c) _____

Write down on the table how many cakes each person bakes using algebraic formulae.

---

3) a) Fill in the table of values and draw the line for:

$$y = \frac{x}{3} - 1$$

It is necessary to choose values that will divide by **3** so that a table of values can be easily created.

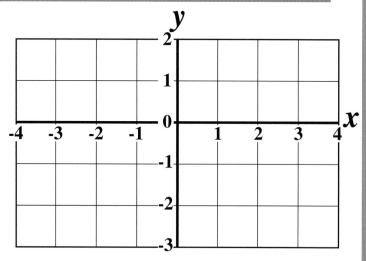

x	-3	0	3
y			

b) Is the gradient of this line negative or positive?

_____

4) Jasmine and Anish play a game with counters. Each child starts with some bags of counters with n counters in each one. The game is a tie so Jasmine and Anish end up with the same number of counters.

Jasmine	**6** bags	lost **10** counters	$6n - 10$
Anish	**4** bags	won **6** counters	$4n + 6$

a) Write an equation to find the value of n:

_____ = _____   b) The value of $n =$ ____

5) Some matchsticks were used to make up squares.

1 square   **2 squares**

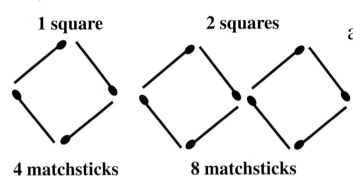

4 matchsticks   **8 matchsticks**

3 squares

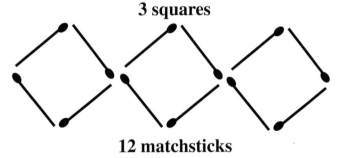

12 matchsticks

a) Write an algebraic rule for the number of matchsticks needed for each square pattern ($m =$ matchsticks and $s =$ squares).

$m =$ _____

b) How many matchsticks will be needed for **10** squares? _____

6) Simplify these expressions: a) $15y \div \text{-}3 =$ ____

b) $3(a + 2) + 2(a + b) - b =$ _____

c) $x - 4y - 3z - 3y + 5z + 2x =$ _____

7) Solve these equations with the balancing method:

a) $4x + 4 = 10x - 8$ b) $5y - 6 = 15 - 2y$

$x =$ ____ $y =$ ____

8) What are the gradients of these lines?

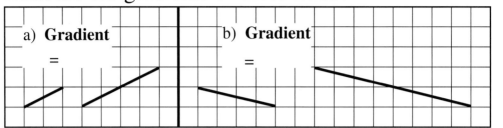

a) **Gradient**

=

b) **Gradient**

=

9) Put the following numbers into this function machine:

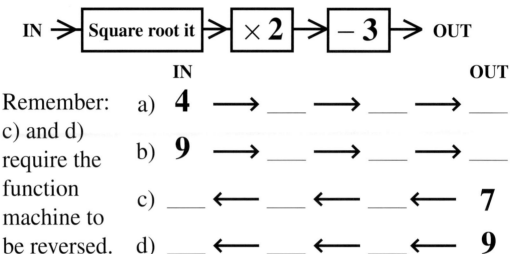

IN →| Square root it |→| ×**2** |→| −**3** |→ OUT

	IN			OUT

Remember: a) **4** ⟶ ___ ⟶ ___ ⟶ ___

c) and d) require the function machine to be reversed.

b) **9** ⟶ ___ ⟶ ___ ⟶ ___

c) ___ ⟵ ___ ⟵ ___ ⟵ **7**

d) ___ ⟵ ___ ⟵ ___ ⟵ **9**

10) a) Draw lines for these two simultaneous equations:

$$y = x - 2 \qquad x + y = 4$$

Score

Fill in the table of values for: $y = x - 2$

x	0	2	4
y			

Use the cover and draw method on:

$$x + y = 4$$

b) Where do the lines meet?

$$x = \underline{\quad} \quad y = \underline{\quad}$$

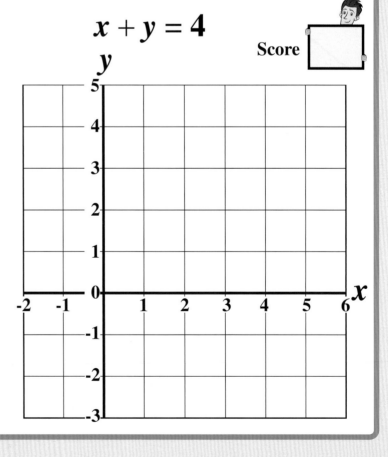

Answers

Chapter Nineteen
Algebra

Exercise 19: 1
1) No 2) Yes 3) Yes
4) No 5) Yes 6) No
7) No 8) No
9) Yes 10) No

Exercise 19: 2
1) 14 2) -13 3) 10
4) -4 5) -3 6) -3
7) -5 8) 5
9) 7 10) 15

Exercise 19: 3
1) 12 2) -3 3) 4
4) -45 5) 21 6) -2
7) 54 8) -2
9) -4 10) -56

Exercise 19: 4
1) -39 2) 63 3) 5
4) -6 5) 18 6) -1
7) -224 8) -16
9) 2 10) 2

Exercise 19: 5
1) $3(3)$ or $-3(-3)$ 2) $2(3+4)$
3) $5(-3+7)$ 4) $4(4+5)$
5) $(3 \times 3) - (3 \times -5) = 24$
6) $(-3 \times 5) + (-3 \times 2) = -21$
7) $(-7 \times -5) + (-7 \times -2) = 49$
8) 10 9) 49 10) 54

Exercise 19: 6
1) 99 2) -6 3) 220
4) 0 5) 32 6) 6
7) 44 8) 12
9) 15 10) 25

Exercise 19: 7a
1) 19 2) 29 3) 28
4) 21 5) 9 6) 85
7) 31 8) 81

Exercise 19: 7b
9) 5 10) 12

Exercise 19: 8
1) − 2) × 3) −
4) ÷ 5) − 6) −
7) + 8) ÷
9) ÷ 10) ×

Exercise 19: 9
1) 8 2) 20
3) 26 4) 165
5) 162 6) 13
7) 65 8) -91
9) 39 10) 104

Exercise 19: 10
1) 375 2) 9
3) 20 4) 24
5) 14 6) 15
7) 6 8) 8
9) 10 10) 14

Exercise 19: 11
1) $\times 11$ or $+70$
2) $\div 8$ or -49
3) $\times 3$ or $+40$
4) $\div 50$ or -196
5) $+52$
6) $\div 3$ 7) $\times 2$ or $+39$
Rule is add 35 then multiply by 2; or add 35 then add 39
8) 84 or 81 9) 9 or 14
10) 100 or 89

Exercise 19: 12
1) 5 2) x and $3y$
3) $3y$ 4) trinomial
5) unlike 6) unlike
7) like 8) unlike
9) unlike 10) like

Exercise 19: 13
1) $6x + 8$ 2) $6y - 5z$
3) $6y - 4z + 9$ 4) $-2a + 7b$
5) $x + 3yz$ 6) $-7y + z$
7) $xyz + 2xy$ 8) $2a - 2b + 4c$
9) $3x + 5y$ 10) $x - 4y + 3z$

Exercise 19: 14
1) $-35x$ 2) xy^2 3) $\frac{5x}{y}$
4) $2y$ 5) $7xy^2$ 6) y^3
7) $\frac{25yx^2}{4}$ 8) $\frac{24x}{-6} = -4x$
9) $2ab^2$ 10) $24xyz$

Exercise 19: 15
1) $4a + 12b$ 2) $5x - 15$
3) $12x + 6y$ 4) $12p^2 + 9pq$
5) $6a + 8b$
6) $3a + 6 + 2a + 2b = 5a + 2b + 6$
7) $4a - 4b - 3a - 3b = a - 7b$
8) $a(3a - 2b)$ 9) $a(b - a)$
10) $3x(3y + 2z)$

Exercise 19: 16
1) $-4x + 5y$ 2) $6x + 4y$
3) $4y + 7z$ 4) $4b - 2a$
5) $2a + 3b$ 6) x
7) $x - 11$ 8) $y + 7$
9) $7y - 3$ 10) $x - 2y - 2z$

Exercise 19: 17
1) 32 2) 30 3) 39 4) -18
5) 14 6) -2 7) 26 8) -10
9) 30 10) 5

Exercise 19: 18
1) 3, 1 2) 625, 3125
3) 16, 18 4) -10, -15
5) 45, 67 or 47, 76 6) 17, 19
7) 5, 2.5 8) 25, 36
9) 720 10) 27, 8

Answers

Exercise 19: 19a
1) a) 66   b) 96
2) a) 101   b) 157

Exercise 19: 19b
3) a) Rule is $2n + 1$
   b) 14th is 29; 19th is 39
4) a) Rule is $4n - 1$
   b) 15th is 59; 32nd is 127
5) a) Rule is $5n + 1$
   b) 12th is 61; 16th is 81

Exercise 19: 19c
6) a) Rule is $5n + 2$
   b) 18th is 92; 29th is 147
7) a) Rule is $6n - 1$
   b) 16th is 95; 38th is 227
8) a) Rule is $6n + 6$
   b) 15th is 96 matches
9) a) Rule is $3n$
   b) 23rd is 69 matches
10) a) Rule is $3n + 1$
   b) 46 matches

Exercise 19: 20a
1) 91   2) 153   3) 378
4) 253   5) 171   6) 300
7) 435   8) 820

Exercise 19: 20b
9) 28 games   10) 15 races

Exercise 19: 21a
1) $x = 3$ 2) $x = 3$
3) $x = 5$ 4) $x = 6$
5) $x = 4$

Exercise 19: 21b
6) $x = 2.2$ 7) $x = 2.7$
8) $x = 3.2$ 9) $x = 1.8$
10) $x = 3.6$

Exercise 19: 22a
1) $y = 3$ 2) $a = 30$
3) $b = 2$ 4) $a = 5$
5) $x = 64$

Exercise 19: 22b
6) $x = 32$ 7) $x = 4$
8) $a = 5$ 9) $y = 4$
10) $x = 2$

Exercise 19: 23a
1) $x = 7$ 2) $x = 9$
3) $x = 54$ 4) $y = 12$

Exercise 19: 23b
5) 2   6) 2   7) 2
8) 3   9) 7   10) 4

Exercise 19: 24a
1) 2   2) 5   3) 1
4) -1   5) 6   6) -7

Exercise 19: 24b
7) $a = 4$ 8) $21 = 21$
   Yes it balances
9) $x = 2$ 10) $-1 = -1$
   Yes it balances

Exercise 19: 25
1) -14 2) 2   3) 6
4) 2   5) 28 6) 20
7) -5   8) -7
9) 3   10) -15

Exercise 19: 26a
1) 19°C   2) 4°C
3) 15°C   4) -11°C
5) 27°C

Exercise 19: 26b
6) 70°F   7) 61°F
8) 36°F   9) 14°F
10) 81°F

Exercise 19: 27
1) $n + 7$ 2) $^b/_8$
3) $2y + x$ 4) $c - 7$
5) $4x - 3$ 6) $y - 5$
7) $\frac{5 + n}{y}$ 8) $\frac{3n - 6}{4}$
9) $\frac{x + 5}{y}$ 10) $^p/_2 - r$

Exercise 19: 28a
1) $^y/_5$ 2) $9x$
3) $50x + 50y$ 4) $\frac{m + e + s}{3}$
5) $52x + 12y$

Exercise 19: 28b
6) a) $^{50}/_x$ b) $^{50}/_x \times 30$
7) a) $y = \frac{x^2}{2} + 3$ b) 11
8) a) i) $2x + 9 = 27$ ii) 9
   b) i) $C = 1200 + 160h$
   ii) £21.60
9) a) £24 b) $y = 30$

Exercise 19: 28c
10) a) i) $2x + 4 = x + 14$
   ii) $x = 10$
   b) i) $4y - 9 = y + 15$ ii) $y = 8$

Exercise 19: 29a
1) a) $x - 11$
   b) i) $r + 10 = 40$ ii) 30
   c) $x = 5$

Exercise 19: 29b
2) Equation: $3x + 14 = 50$
   Zak scores 12 goals,
   Murrey scores 17 goals
   and Philip scores 21 goals.
3) Equation: $4x + 64 = 144$
   Brighde collects 58 stamps,
   Nichol collects 37 stamps,
   Rory collects 29 stamps
   & Holly collects 20 stamps.

Exercise 19: 29c
4) a) $3(x + y + z)$ b) $2(a + b)$
   c) $24akm$ d) $2(5y + 8)m$

Exercise 19: 29d
5) a) i) $2n^2$ ii) $6n$
   b) $3xy$ c) $(6x^2 + 4x)$sq.m.
   d) i) Area = $6y \times 2y$
   ii) $12y^2$sq.m   iii) $16y$
   e) i) $5xy$ ii) 30cm²

Exercise 19: 29e
6) a) $125x^3$ cubic cm
   b) $30y^3$ cubic m
   c) $67,500z^3$ cubic mm

Answers

Exercise 19: 29f

7) a) $r + b + g = 7$

   b) $r = 4$; $b = 2$; $g = 1$

Exercise 19: 29g

8) a) $y = 2x$ b) i) $6s + 3$ ii) $s = 17$

9) a) i) $2x + 6$ & $3x + 5$

    ii) $2x + 6$

  b) i) $y = 5$

    ii) $2y = 4z + x$

Exercise 19: 29h

10) Statement e) $10o = 8a$

Exercise 19: 30a

1) Line A

2) Line B

x	2	1	-1
y	3	1	-3

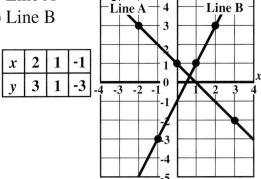

Exercise 19: 30b

3) $y = 2$ 4) $y = x$

5) $x = -3$ 6) $y = -x$

Exercise 19: 30c

7) $y = 3x$

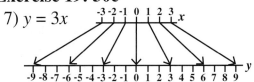

8) $y = x - 3$

x	-2	-1	0	1	2	3
y	-5	-4	-3	-2	-1	0

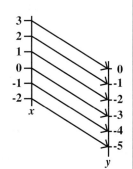

9) $y = x^2$

x	0	1	2	3	4
y	0	1	4	9	16

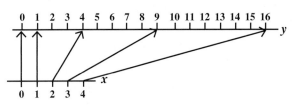

10) $y = 3x - 1$

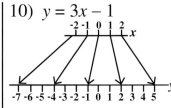

x	-2	-1	0	1	2
y	-7	-4	-1	2	5

Exercise 19: 31a

1) $y = 3x - 2$

a)

x	0	1	2
y	-2	1	4

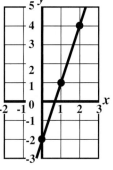

b) Positive

2) $y = {}^x/_2 - 1$

a) Any 3 columns

x	-4	-2	0	2
y	-3	-2	-1	0

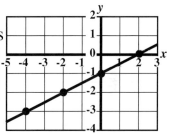

b) Positive

Any 3 of the 4 points plotted

Exercise 19: 31b

3) $3x - 5y = 15$

a)

b) Positive

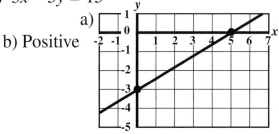

4) $2x + 5y = -10$

a)

b) Negative

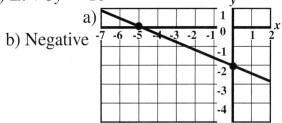

Exercise 19: 31c

5) $y = -2x$ a)

b) Negative

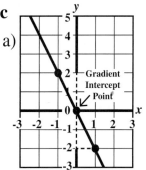

Answers

6) $y = {}^x/_2 + 2$

a)

b) Positive

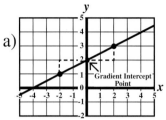

Exercise 19: 31d

7) $y = x^2 + 1$

x	-3	-2	-1	0	1	2	3
y	10	5	2	1	2	5	10

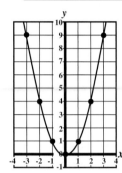

8) $y = x^2$

x	-3	-2	-1	0	1	2	3
y	9	4	1	0	1	4	9

Exercise 19: 31e

9) $y = 5 - x^2$

x	-3	-2	-1	0	1	2	3
y	-4	1	4	5	4	1	-4

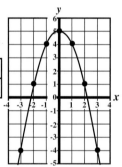

Exercise 19: 31f

10) $y = x^3 + 3$

x	-3	-2	-1	0	1	2	3
y	-24	-5	2	3	4	11	30

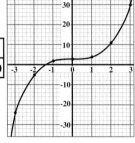

Exercise 19: 32a

1) $y = 2x - 2$

x	0	1	2
y	-2	0	2

$y = x + 1$

x	0	1	2
y	1	2	3

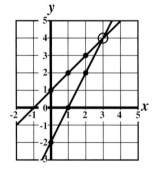

The solution is $x = 3$; $y = 4$

2) The solution is
   $x = -3$; $y = 4$

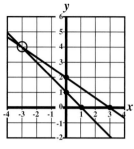

Exercise 19: 32b

3) $x = 5$; $y = 2$ 4) $x = 5$; $y = 3$
5) $a = 6$; $b = -4$ 6) $x = 3$; $y = 1$

Exercise 19: 32c

7) $3c + 5i = 630$ $4c + 3i = 510$
8) cola $(c) = 60$p ice cream $(i) = 90$p
9) $6t + 48p = 138$ $5t + 22p = 70$
10) Pupils $(p) = £2.50$
    Teachers $(t) = £3.00$

Exercise 19: 33

1) 2   2) -1   3) -3   4) $-{}^1/_5$
5) $^1/_2$ 6) $y = 4x + 1$ 7) $y = -{}^1/_2x + 1$
8) $y = x + 2$ 9) $y = 3x + 2$
10) a) $3x + 6y = 18$ b) $2x - 7y = 14$

Exercise 19: 34

1) a) Seneesh with $5x + 7$ b) 22
2) a) $c + 4$ b) $3c$ c) $3c - 5$
3) $y = {}^x/_3 - 1$

a)
x	-3	0	3
y	-2	-1	0

b) Positive

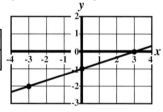

4) a) $6n - 10 = 4n + 6$ b) $n = 8$
5) a) $4s$ b) 40 matchsticks
6) a) $-5y$ b) $5a + b + 6$ c) $3x - 7y + 2z$
7) a) $x = 2$ b) $y = 3$
8) a) $^1/_2$ b) $-^1/_4$
9) a) 1   b) 3   c) 25   d) 36
10) a) $y = x - 2$

x	0	2	4
y	-2	0	2

b) The lines meet
   at $x = 3$; $y = 1$

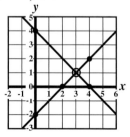

PROGRESS CHARTS

Shade in your score for each exercise on the graph. Add up for your total score. If there are
a) b) c) etc. parts to a question, all parts must be correct to gain a mark.

19. ALGEBRA

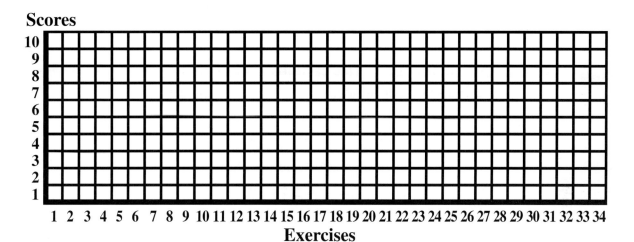

Scores

Exercises

Total Score

Percentage

%

CERTIFICATE OF

ACHIEVEMENT

This certifies

_____

has successfully completed

11+ Maths
Year 5–7
WORKBOOK **6**

Overall percentage
score achieved

%

Comment _____

_____

Signed _____

(teacher/parent/guardian)

Date _____